Praise

'This is a compel.......g .... , ...gy, ...m·
its beginnings to the future, uniquely situated in the
context of the UK solar boom of the past decade.
John shares his personal journey, which has taken
him from the black of oil, coal and fossil fuels to the
green and clean technologies of renewables. John's
passion for renewables is highly contagious, and
his call to fight to save the plant is powerful. His
inspiring book is particularly accessible to those with
little to no knowledge of solar energy and gives great
insight into the what, the who and the why of the UK
solar boom. Buckle up and enjoy this solar coaster!'
> — **Arnoud C Klaren**, Head of Projects,
> Quintas Advisory

'This is a comprehensive but easy-to-read book
about the solar-powered universe. It provides
in-depth knowledge, particularly for those entering
the professional solar business, as well as detailed
insights about advanced testing, well-explained
benefits and technical approaches. I'm often
surprised when I speak to people in the industry to
find how little they actually know about solar and
how the sector works. This book will bring everyone
up to speed. I would highly recommend it as a must-
read for everyone in the utility-scale solar industry.'
> — **Erik Lohse**, solar quality expert and creator
> of the MBJ Mobile Lab

'This is a must-read textbook for the utility-scale solar PV industry. John articulates clearly and dives deep into the details, addressing the issues and providing applicable solutions. Whether you are a newcomer to the industry or a seasoned professional, this book is the one you will always refer back to.'
— **Ypatios Moysiadis**, managing partner, Wattcrop, and postgraduate lecturer, City University

SOLAR BOOM

The insider's guide
to the utility-scale
solar industry

JOHN DAVIES CEng

R^ethink

First published in Great Britain in 2021
by Rethink Press (www.rethinkpress.com)

This book is dedicated to my beautiful wife, Sara Wyn, to my children, Felix and Florence, to my family and friends, to my mentors and supporters, and to every reader who wants to make a positive change in the world.

Contents

Introduction

The climate and ecological emergency

Global warming and climate change are real. They're not a hoax, a conspiracy or a money-making scheme. The climate and ecological emergency is the biggest threat to civilisation the world has ever faced, and we're seeing its effects on our weather patterns right now all over the planet. If we do not tackle the causes of this change, the world will face large-scale human displacement, disease, famine, loss of ecosystems and ultimately mass extinction.

The biggest contributing factor to atmospheric warming and climatic effects is greenhouse gas emissions, which are released into the atmosphere in many forms. Proportionally, CO_2 is the most-emitted gas, and it comes predominantly from the burning of fossil fuels to power our homes, industries and transportation. This, together with the devastation of oxygen-generating forests and jungles, is causing the polar ice caps to melt, sea levels to rise and extreme weather events to take place more often all over the world.

There are other major contributors to rising atmospheric temperatures, including industrial-scale agriculture – in particular, deforestation – to clear land for growing crops to feed the world's exponentially growing appetite for meat. This expansion in livestock, as well as an uptrend in waste food and biodegradable materials, is generating huge volumes of methane, which is eighty-four times more damaging to the atmosphere than CO_2 in the short term.[1]

Additionally, the global fishing industry is systematically wiping out aquatic ecosystems by uncontrolled over-fishing. Cathedral-sized trawling nets destroy whatever is in their path, including CO_2-absorbing submarine vegetation as well as sharks, whales and dolphins – all considered 'by-kill'. If current fishing trends continue, we will see virtually empty oceans by the year 2048.[2] This doesn't just mean no more fish; the ripple effect on the human civilisation will be widely felt and devastating.

Over the last century or so, through scientific data collection, we have identified the main contributing factors to global warming. The world is gaining an understanding of the situation, but this isn't happening fast enough. Activists, educators and influential celebrities are starting to penetrate the GDP-focused governments around the world, and policies being implemented are starting to move the needle – or at least starting to slow the effects of global warming. In the West, there is a cultural and ethical shift towards being more sustainable, using renewable power, buying electric vehicles, making diet improvements and recycling more. However, we need to do more, and soon, to avoid a series of catastrophic tipping points.

Considering everything we must do to reverse the effects of global warming, it makes me frustrated and overwhelmed, wondering what I can do, what my family and business can do, to combat global warming at scale. Surely one person can't have a measurable effect on 100 years of atmospheric pollution, warming oceans and global weather patterns, can they?

My view is that the power and will of the people will make change possible. We need to realign the collective attitudes and motivations of modern society, supercharge people and incentivise them to change. The world's greed for wealth, power and convenience, and our old work-eat-sleep-repeat habits, have failed us – and future generations. If we don't change in the next decade, when we know that global warming reversal is possible, then we've had it.

I started my climate change engineering business (2DegreesKelvin) and wrote this book to try to make a difference. If I can share my learnings from within the utility-scale solar industry – which will be the backbone of clean energy in the future – if I can influence the development, construction and operational phases of solar asset life cycles to make solar more sustainable, and if I can encourage new solar professionals into the industry, then I've made a positive change in the world.

Let me give you some context about where my passion for solar, renewables and making a difference comes from.

From black to green

When structuring this book, I wanted to include a summary of how my view on the world has developed and crystalised along my journey. To be able to share my love of solar photovoltaics (PV) with the world and educate and encourage new professionals entering the sector is a true privilege. This book is the accumulation of ten years of field experience, and it has been a dream of mine for over two years, along with creating 2DegreesKelvin – a carbon neutral, climate change engineering company.

My journey started in Tasmania. For those of you who are not great at geography, this is the small island below Australia. My Welsh father emigrated to Australia with his mother at the age of fifteen. My mother was born in Melbourne and moved to Hobart (in Tasmania) with her family due to her father's job in the wool trade. I migrated back to the UK with my family while I was still in nappies, and I grew up in the small villages by the coast and surrounded by countryside down in the southwest corner of Wales. My childhood included making dens in the woods and dams in streams, jumping off the rocks into the sea, fishing for mackerel on my uncle's boat and poking cow pats with sticks. I suppose I took it all for granted as a child – the freedom to explore the coast-line, coastal paths and woods, to know the names for different trees and flowers, to catch tadpoles and sticklebacks in the stream, and to see how many daddy-long-legs I could fit in the palm of my hands. In hindsight, it was clear that my life purpose was going to be linked with my love for the environment, nature and science.

During my early years, I lived near the Milford Haven Waterway – a world-famous oil and gas terminal and estuary in the Welsh county of Pembrokeshire, and one of the deepest natural harbours in the world. The *Sea Empress* oil disaster in the mid-90 s had a profound impact on me. The ship tragically spilt 72,000 tonnes of crude oil, devastating the Pembrokeshire Coast National Park – one of the most important marine and wildlife conservation areas in Europe – and killing tens of thousands of birds and marine creatures.[3]

My father had an engineering company that relied on the abundance of work from the surrounding oil refineries and gas terminals, and this is where I got my start working in industry. Labouring, painting, scraping, litter picking, strimming, fire watching – you name it, I did it. Through it all, there was an undertone of oil and gas on the wind.

After secondary school, I studied Mechanical Engineering at Swansea University. Like many people, at this stage I did not know what I wanted to do with my life or who I wanted to become. I just knew that I was interested in engineering, and I looked for interesting graduate jobs which I could throw myself into. My first professional role was graduate engineer, working for a company specialising in coal-fired power station maintenance and projects. There was a massive learning curve, particularly with the management of welders, fitters, and other tradespeople, and planning and delivering complex projects. At this early stage in my career, I was aware of global warming and climate change, but it wasn't on my radar as a major issue, and I didn't see myself as contributing much towards it in any good or bad way. Little did I know that the very industries I'd been specialising in were two of the worst contributors to global warming (oil and gas, and coal).

After working on projects on the road for a couple of years, I wanted to move back to where I now called home: Cardiff, the capital city of Wales. Becoming an engineering manager and then a power station manager at the relatively young age of twenty-eight, I was thrust into a position of responsibility with 120 staff, a board of directors to report to, and three power generation units that provided critical power to the national grid and distribution networks in the South Wales area. Uskmouth Power Station was commissioned in the late 1950s, and at that time it was the oldest operating coal-fired power station in the UK. It was still reliable, but, at over fifty years old, it was nearing the end of its life and the asset owners started to explore the possibilities of converting this fossil fuel relic into a more sustainable form of power generation: biomass (pelletised wood). In 2011, I transferred roles to head up this biomass conversion project, and for the first time I became excited about renewables and more aware of subsidy schemes, global warming, climate change and the direction I wanted to travel in with my career. Unfortunately, the conversion did not go ahead at that time, but at the time of writing, a decade later, it has recently been announced that the conversion is back on. This time, though, instead of biomass, the planned fuel source is a waste-derived fuel.

Following that aborted project, I entered the world of 'energy-from-waste' and joined the construction team building a new power plant fuelled by municipal (black bin bag) waste. I was responsible for recruiting and training the new operations team to run the plant. I designed, developed and implemented the operating procedures and business management systems, and I liaised with the environmental agency on their permit implementation plans. I learnt a great deal from this role about the lengthy processes that thermal combustion technologies need to undertake to comply with emissions-to-atmosphere regulations. These measures have come a long way (in the UK, at least), over the last couple of decades, and regulations are now more robust. I also took part in several risk management processes, such as hazard operability (HAZOP) studies, where I chaired pre-design-freeze sessions that were critical to the safe design of the plant.

The company I was working for offered me an opportunity to start a new division focused on solar PV and energy storage. This was where I found my true passion in life: my love for renewables, and in particular solar PV. After several years in solar, I plucked up enough courage to start my own business. In 2019, I launched 2DegreesKelvin, a climate neutral, engineering services company specialising in solar farm assessments, testing, improvements and optimisation. In designing this business concept, I drew on my market knowledge and the information I gathered from visiting over 10% of the UK solar fleet. I saw a gap in the market for a company that could provide specialist support services to the whole supply chain. A company that would dedicate itself to becoming a global authority on solar farm revamping and repowering. A company that was carbon neutral and invested in innovation and great people. A company that would make a measurable positive impact on global warming and climate change.

When I tell people about my company, '2DegreesKelvin', I often get asked, 'Who's Kelvin?' The name is a nod to the historic United Nations Paris Agreement signed by 196 nations in 2015. This agreement 'aims to substantially reduce global greenhouse gas emissions in an effort to limit the global temperature increase in this century to 2 degrees Celsius above pre-industrial levels, while pursuing the means to limit the increase to 1.5 degrees'.[4] Unfortunately, based on current projections and the lack of urgency from world leaders and governments, the realist in me believes that the 1.5-degrees-limit target will be broken in the next couple of decades. Despite various countries' efforts – and the UK are among the world leaders in implementing proactive carbon emission reduction legislative targets – the biggest contributors (America, China and India) don't seem to be moving away from fossil fuels quickly enough. For me, it's all about the 2-degree-limit target, which is the point of no return, where we will reach global-scale tipping points such as Greenland melting, and there's no coming back from events like that.

As a chartered engineer and a nerd at heart, I recalled that in my thermodynamic calculations in my uni days I used Kelvin as the base unit for temperature. Degrees Celsius and degrees Kelvin are the same scale unit, but zero degrees Celsius is 273.15 degrees Kelvin. Thus, 2DegreesKelvin was born: a company designed to keep the world underneath this critical 2-degree threshold in average atmospheric temperature increase.

My journey has taken me from the black of oil, coal and fossil fuels to the green and clean technologies of renewables. From now on in my career, I want to deliver services and solutions which will make a difference. I'm not happy to sit inside my comfort zone; I want to keep pushing towards a greener and cleaner world for future generations. One of my reasons for writing this book was to make people aware of the large-scale solar industry and the pivotal role it will play in the world's attempts to mitigate CO_2 emissions. I hope to educate professionals and encourage them to join our fight to save the planet.

One of my biggest frustrations is the world's obsession with fossil fuels and fossil-fuel-derived products.

Most of us use these products every day – they are everywhere – but how did we get to this point? Our desire for convenience has underwritten the global domination of the oil, gas and energy giants. The political and financial power that these corporate giants have is truly concerning. It's not unstoppable, but it's the hardest thing to stop in our modern world. Governments are blindly encouraging and subsidising our greed, all for the good of the markets. Add to this the collective stubbornness of society who generally don't like being told how to live their lives, what to eat and how to travel, and we have a complex and arduous path ahead of us. You may be thinking, 'You're a hypocrite.' Yes, I've worked in oil refineries and power stations, and my family has been funded by these industries indirectly for decades. But that doesn't mean that I can't change direction. We all have the power to make better choices. To select renewable energy power suppliers. To commit to our next cars being electric. To live our lives in a more sustainable way.

A world powered by 100% renewables is possible. A world that consumes sustainable products and food is possible. A world that doesn't pollute its air, land and water, a world without plastics – a world that we have performed CPR on, brought back from the brink of death, and that we will cherish and take care of for generations to come – is all possible. The power is in our hands; if money needs to be lost and power needs to be eroded, that's a small price to pay to save our planet.

Goals and takeaways

This book focuses on solar PV's rise to becoming the cheapest and cleanest form of energy in the world. The 2010s saw unprecedented global adoption of solar PV, which is a positive step towards meeting our CO_2 reduction targets. However, in our haste, we made mistakes and missed processes, and huge numbers of operational solar assets are underperforming and may not last their full design-life period or fulfil their clean and green energy promise.

In the following pages, I present insights from ten years of field-based PV experience and a further ten years in heavy industry in layman's terms to educate, influence and positively affect existing stakeholders in the industry and the decisions they make, as well as informing newcomers looking to join the renewables revolution.

This book is structured in three parts. Part One, The Solar Coaster, sets the scene with solar PV as a disruptive and world-changing technology, covering where it came from, the principals of the technology itself, solar sectors and applications, who's who in the solar market, and the resource and competency gaps which have formed as the industry finishes its first decade in the sun.

Part Two, Solar Assets, begins by exploring operational assets, areas of your solar asset which may be costing you power and revenue, the road to repowering solar assets and site optimisation suitability. The later chapters in Part Two then focus on new-build assets, the importance of quality management services, proactive testing, CAPEX versus OPEX and lessons learnt from the subsidy-driven solar boom.

Part Three offers a glimpse into the future of solar PV and explores where the technology can go. Which technology and innovation trends can enable solar PV to lead the way in making the world 100% renewable powered? Part Three also discusses artificial intelligence (AI) and robots, blockchain and decommissioning, which will all help solar PV contribute to decarbonising the world's energy needs.

If you work in the solar industry or want to get into solar energy to join the climate emergency revolution, then this book is for you. As well as providing an overview of the sector and technology, it also offers insights into maximising your operational and new-build solar assets' return on investment (ROI) and provides a lookahead into a positive future powered by clean, green and affordable energy sources.

After reading this book, you will have a better understanding of the utility solar sector, the main areas of concern, the mistakes we've made in the past and what we can learn from them, and how we can improve our operational and new-build assets. You'll understand how utility-scale solar can be higher-quality, safer and more profitable, with assets that last for their full design life. You should also feel uplifted by the role that solar PV will have in all our futures. Let the sun shine.

PART ONE

THE SOLAR COASTER

It's been one hell of a ride so far on 'the solar coaster'. The 2010s was a decade of diminishing government subsidies, winter construction, price wars, and learning how to deploy and maintain utility-scale solar on the fly. This has created a volatile but exciting market which has suffered great highs and lows.

Part One of this book introduces solar as a renewable form of energy, describes the main components of a solar PV system, explores the applications of solar PV, offers a who's who of the utility solar industry and uncovers some of the lessons learnt from the subsidy-fuelled 'solar boom'.

1

The History Of Solar

Before we look at what has been achieved and what we can do better in the future to ensure solar PV is deployed as efficiently as possible and will last its intended project life cycle, we should first understand where it all came from.

Simple solar

Solar is simple, right? A static, fix-and-forget technology which generates clean and green energy, can be incorporated into natural habitats, and provides a handsome return for its investors. It needs little maintenance and nothing ever goes wrong. Well, it's not as simple as everyone thought.

Into a developing international solar market, introduce renewable subsidies and you have a recipe for a national 'solar boom', which brings with it widespread solar PV adoption and deployment on the positive side but many issues, challenges and opportunities to learn from mistakes on the other.

The concept of PV energy dates back to William Grylls Adams and a student of his, Richard Day, in 1876. They found that when selenium was exposed to sunlight, it produced electricity. Selenium cells were proven to be inefficient and after over seventy-five years of lab-based experimentation and development, Calvin Fuller, Gerald Pearson and Daryl Chapin discovered the early silicon cell we are familiar with today in 1953. Many decades of R&D followed to improve the efficiency, price, and design of solar cells and modules. Solar PV only became a credible technology at the turn of the twenty-first century.[5]

Let there be light

The source of solar energy is light. Light – or, in solar language, 'irradiance' – lands on the Earth following its 150-million-kilometre journey from our sun.[6] Visible light is electromagnetic radiation within the portion of the electromagnetic spectrum that can be perceived by the human eye. Sunlight provides the energy that green plants use to create sugars and starches, which release energy into the living things that digest them. This process, known as photosynthesis, provides virtually all the energy used by living things on this planet. According to the World Meteorological Organization, 'The Earth absorbs most of the energy reaching its surface, a small fraction is reflected. In total, approximately 70% of incoming radiation is absorbed by the atmosphere and the Earth's surface while around 30% is reflected back to space.'[7] The light that falls on the land and sea of our beautiful Earth equates to 122 petawatts of energy – that's 122,000,000,000,000,000,000 watts of energy in the form of light – every day.[8] As The World Counts states: 'In less than 80 minutes solar energy equivalent to total world energy use for a full year strikes Earth, meaning that the sun could power the world almost 7,000 times.'[9] This abundance leads to the suggestion that it will not be long before solar energy will become the world's primary energy source. Why not? It's free, abundant, clean – and, for the next few hundred million years, sustainable.

2

What Is Photovoltaic Technology?

In this chapter, we take a closer look at the basics of photovoltaic (PV) technology. Firstly, you need a solar cell, and there are several modern technologies out there. The three most popular are polycrystalline, monocrystalline and thin film. A monocrystalline cell is exposed to irradiation (light), which creates a pair of positive and negative electrical charges. These charges are separated by a junction field, which produces a current and a voltage, and multiplying the current by the voltage gives you the power of the cell. This power wants to flow towards the nearest conductor and conveniently positioned 'grid fingers', which are thin silver wires usually positioned throughout the light-receiving material which conduct this power. These grid fingers are connected to larger conductors in the form of busbars which carry the current onward to the next cell in the module in series. Other cell and module technologies are configured in slightly different ways, but they all use the sun's light to create a positive DC (direct current) electrical charge.

Here we look at the components of a solar system.

Modules

The majority of the world's installed solar is currently sixty-cell mono or poly modules (at 220–320 W per module). Over the last few years, module technology has advanced to enable larger, more efficient modules that are often made up of 72 cells or 144 half-cell configurations (ranging from 300–600 W per module).

These modules are generally arranged in strings, meaning that a number of modules are connected in series (positive to negative, much like batteries in a toy), and the entire string of modules will either come back to a string inverter or to a string combiner box before going back to a centralised inverter.

Inverters

The purpose of the inverter (or converter, as they are sometimes called) is to convert DC power, generated in the solar modules, to AC (alternating current) power which can be exported to the electrical network or consumed on an industrial site. Inverters are electro-mechanical devices which do the bulk of the work on a solar system. The modules just sit there and heat up and cool down, expand and contract, whereas the inverters are cycled hard every day of their operational life.

The inverter size and type depend on several factors, but as a rule of thumb, large sites over 5MWp (megawatt peak) normally have larger centralised inverters for areas of a solar farm or installation, whereas smaller installations might use string inverters for smaller areas of the installation. There is a shift nowadays to install smart string inverters on large sites, and this will be discussed later in the book. There are pros and cons for each; for example, the centrals may be cheaper (per/Wp), but if they break down larger areas of the installation will be unavailable. String inverters are usually slightly less reliable (apart from a few manufacturers at the top end of the market) and, as there are multiple units to service, they take more effort to maintain, but they create fewer losses when they do go down.

Transformers

Once the DC power is converted into AC and suitably stepped up via a transformer, it can be exported onto the local network, although this isn't the case in domestic-scale installs. In the UK, in most cases larger installations are connected at 11 kilovolts (kV) and sometimes 33kV, which both fall under the control of the district network operator (DNO). The distribution network as a priority distributes energy around its particular regional turf, and then it feeds into the national grid transmission network. In these cases, it must step up to 66kV, 132kV and 275kV. There are rare installations in the UK which are connected directly to the national grid at 66kV and 132kV, but these are only for large sites. There are various distribution and transition network designs and connection ratings all around the world, but many follow this general configuration.

Mounting structures

Mounting structures vary widely from fixed and ballasted roof mount systems to pile driven or screw fixed vertical pillars in ground mount systems. The primary role of mounting structures is to fix the solar modules to the roof or the ground. They need to consider wind and snow loadings, as well as thermal expansion and contraction. They can also act as channels or aboveground routes for cabling heading back to the inverters and beyond.

Fixed mounting structures are available at a variety of inclination angles. The design will specify the angle of inclination, which is dependent on module configuration, space between the rows, latitude, site topologies and other factors. Typically, inclination in Western Europe is between fifteen and thirty degrees.

The other relevant consideration for mounting structures is tracking systems. These are single- or multi-axis motorised systems which keep the modules perpendicular (or as close as possible to perpendicular) to the sun. This maximises yield; however, historically they have been significantly more expensive than other mounting structures and have a reputation for being unreliable due to the mechanical moving parts, which often break down. These systems appear to be coming down in cost and improving their reliability year on year, so you may see tracking systems becoming more popular in the future, even in less sunny climates.

In terms of utility-scale solar today in the UK, feasibility studies are generally looking into three system configurations on which to run simulations: fixed tilt, south facing; fixed tilt, east/west facing; and single-axis trackers. Trackers are generally obtaining higher yields but less installed capacity, and therefore less annual production on a given land parcel.

Earthing

For the safety of personnel and the asset itself, a solar farm must be suitably earthed. It's not as simple as connecting it to the ground; detailed earthing studies are required in the first instance to determine the soil resistivity, and this – as well as the layout of the plant and the various low-, medium- and high-voltage zones – will determine the earthing design. On a utility-scale solar farm, the earthing design usually consists of a network of area- or equipment-based earthing grids; a system connecting mounting structure rows and tables together; and, in most cases, the metal perimeter fencing system connected to multiple earthing rod electrodes. The detail around fixing methods, lugs and connectors is important; as is clear labelling (a technical adviser bugbear), particularly where different metal materials (such as aluminium and steel) are in contact. I recommend involving an earthing specialist in the early stages of solar farm earthing system site development and design.

Cabling

In terms of the various types of cables used on a given solar installation, cable engineering, design and specifications are a complex and evolving topic. In the case of a solar system, you generally have DC and AC cabling. DC (direct current) is used from the modules to the inverters and AC (alternating current) is used from the inverters outward to your connection point. The design for a 5MWp plant, for example, would consist of tens of kilometres of DC and AC cable. DC cables are generally either 4 mm or 6 mm cross-sectional area fine multistranded copper conductors which have an outer insulation sheath which resists

UV degradation, used between modules, strings, string inverters and string combiner boxes. In solar, outer sheaths used to be coloured red and black as visual aids for which cable was positive and which cable was negative, but manufacturers phased them out due to additives in the red-coated DC cables and their premature degradation. You also have much larger-dimension DC cables leading from the string inverters or string combiner boxes away to either the substations or centralised inverters, respectively, as well as AC cables with larger cross-sectional areas and which vary more widely due to the many types of inverters, operational conditions and connection situations. The other main variance with cables is the conductor material. Traditionally these have been made of copper, but due to inflated costs for this material, there is a move towards aluminium, which is cheaper.

Most issues regarding cables on a solar installation will be from the DC side. The majority of those will be insulation resistance (R_{ISO}), where current flowing within these cables leaks to earth. In such cases, there is a pathway through the cable's sheath and outer coating material to ground. Particularly in wet conditions, when the current can flow from the inner conductor through to earth this will cause R_{ISO} faults, inverter trips, losses in production, and health and safety risks of electrocution. Most of the issues we have found in the field point to cuts or nicks in the cables, usually caused during the installation process, or the premature breakdown of cable protection causing cracking or thinning. This is an area of quality control which needs more attention from new-build site owners and constructors.

Connectors

DC cable connectors, widely known as MC4 connectors, are the small, moulded plastic connector joints connecting multiple modules together in a string. There was a need to develop a universal connector which could be connected and unconnected easily as required but which would also form a strong, watertight electrical connection. Before the current MC4 connector, there was the MC3 and many other prior variations.

As these components are moulded pieces of plastic with a couple of easy-to-copy inner metal parts, 'clone' connectors have been reverse engineered and sold around the world as 'MC4 compatible' connectors. These clone connectors are alarmingly common and are often found during an investigation on a site suffering from R_{ISO} earth leakage issues. We have found clone connectors which literally crumble in your hands, leaving exposed live conductors. This is not only a reliability and production issue but a ticking time bomb in terms of electrocution risk and fire safety (particularly on rooftop installations).

The important point here is to always connect the same type of connector together. Even if module manufacturer A and manufacturer B both have their own brand of DC connectors which are 'MC4 compatible', if you connect two different types together, the risk of faults is significantly higher. These low-cost parts have massive impacts on power production, availability and safety.

The method and standard of installation is just as important as the quality and provenance of the connector itself. Most modules come as standard with approved and vetted connectors (via module manufacturers), but when additional connectors are required in the field you must install them in line with the installation manual (relating to that specific connector) and using the correct tools and equipment – not just a pair of pliers or your teeth.

Most solar-related fires worldwide are due to the premature breakdown or poor installation of MC4 connectors. If you use vetted, traceable connectors and install them correctly, then fires shouldn't occur, and owners can avoid production losses.

String combiner boxes

String combiner boxes (SCBs) are typically used on solar farms with centralised inverters. They are Ingress Protection (IP) rated, secured electrical cabinets where a collection of positive and negative DC string cables will be routed. They will contain a main isolation switch and a pair of fuses for each string tail, all of which provide electrical protection and isolation. All of the strings are connected in parallel to a common positive and negative busbar, and this busbar is connected to larger DC positive and negative cables which are routed underground to the centralised inverters. The SCB is where an operative would conduct electrical testing of the strings as well as a safe isolation.

Switchgear and protection relays

In all energy generation systems, you will find switchgear and protection relays. These are essential safety disconnect switches that protect, control and isolate high-voltage (HV) circuits. This equipment is used either to de-energise (providing safe electrical isolation) or to clear faults further downstream in the system.

Switchgear and protection relays are specified for the capacity, loading and function required on a system-by-system basis. They can be programmed or set to function under certain system operational or fault conditions, all with the primary function of protecting human life and the equipment itself.

In power generation systems which are connected to the network or national grid, there is a requirement for a special type of additional relay (switch), which is the final barrier between the power generation system and the outer network. In the UK, this additional relay is called a 'G59' (or more recently a 'G99') relay, and a fault on the site which could affect the outside network, or a fault on the outside network which could affect the site, will trip this relay and flatten the site. Often, if work is required on the outside network within the same geographical location as a solar farm, the G59 or G99 relay will trip to ensure that energy cannot make its way onto that circuit. There are many reasons why such a relay would trip, including on-site transformer faults, network lightning strikes or even bird strikes.

G59 and G99 relays are often fitted with a programable 'auto-reclose' function. This function will keep checking the circuit (both sides) for the same fault that tripped it, and once cleared it will auto-reclose the switch, allowing the solar system to re-energise. However, in some cases these relays either do not have this auto-reclose function (meaning that each time it trips an operative will need to go to the site to manually reset it) or they only have a single auto-reclose (meaning that it would only reclose itself once). I strongly recommend that you invest in G59 or G99 relays with multiple auto-reclose capabilities. They will pay for themselves in avoiding any system downtime in a single event.

Metering

The main purpose of a meter on a solar installation, much like the electrical meters in your homes, is to measure the amount of electricity consumed or generated. If you install solar panels on your roof at home, there will be some days in the summer at maximum generation where your meter will slow down, stop entirely or even go in reverse – meaning that you are feeding power outward onto the network. On a solar farm, the primary function of a meter is to capture the amount of renewable energy generated in kilowatt hours (kWh). This information is then shared with the regulator (OFGEM, the Office of Gas and Electricity Markets, in the UK) as evidence of renewable power generation for any subsidies that a site may have. The data is also used as evidence of the power which is sold in the merchant market or as part of a power purchase agreement (PPA).

SCADA and communications systems

Supervisory control and data acquisition, or SCADA, is the brain of the solar system. Through a network of data and control system cables, computers, communication hubs and user interfaces, it enables the site to be observed, and in some cases operated, remotely.

Early solar systems did not contain SCADA systems, meaning that these generation plants were running blind. The only indication of whether your system was operating or not was whether it was generating or not, and the meter would generally confirm this. You may have been able to compare seasonal or monthly totals of generation, but that was it – no intelligence, foresight or awareness of what was going on.

In modern SCADA systems of solar installations, an operator or owner will have access to a live operational dashboard showing the generation-related parameters and even a digital representation of the solar system itself showing faults and issues, right down to bird droppings on an individual solar panel. This is a powerful tool as it significantly reduces the operations and maintenance (O&M) requirements; you only need to go on-site when it's absolutely necessary. A SCADA system enables an operator or owner to track emerging issues as a form of predictive maintenance as well as create a lifelong operational and maintenance record which will age with the asset.

SCADA and communications systems, however, are notorious for reliability issues. 'Comms issues' are by far the most common 'fault' captured on a solar farm. In many cases, SCADA and communications systems rely on the 3G or 4G satellite network, and this causes frequent issues. Even when the system is connected to a permanently connected line, there are reliability issues with servers, modems and control electronics. These issues create unnecessary callouts to operators, often requiring them to rush to site only to turn the

system off and back on again. It is therefore impera-
tive to invest in reliable, top-quality SCADA and
communications systems.

CCTV and security systems

Closed-circuit television (CCTV) and security systems
are only a requirement for large solar plants. For
rooftop installations, the fact that they are on a roof
deters thieves from attempting to steal the equipment; however, on a solar farm, from an insurance
and investor requirement perspective, CCTV systems
are a must.

In the early days of the solar boom in the UK (2011–
2012), sites didn't have much security beyond a fence
and a locked gate. The value of the modules and the
copper in the cables on such sites may have been too
tempting for thieves (regardless of electrocution risk),
and many sites were broken into in this period.

Modern UK plants are usually fitted with a 2.4 m
fence around the perimeter of the site, thermal and /
or night-vision imagery cameras in a point-to-point
spread around the perimeter of the site with motion
detection, and a CCTV company monitoring any
activated alarms 24/7. A big issue is the presence of
wildlife on a solar farm. Whether it be birds, rabbits,
foxes, badgers or wild stock such as sheep located on
the solar farm, all animal movements activate motion

detection alarms, meaning lots of false events which the monitoring teams and O&M companies need to deal with. This is why modern systems incorporate computer learning analytics which can identify the shape of a given moving object and ensure that only bodies shaped like a human will activate the alarm.

Once the system detects a human-shaped object, it activates the live monitoring of a solar farm by the monitoring company, which will have a series of contacts to call. The first step in the escalation sequence is to request confirmation (or not) of a known person on-site. If the conclusion is that it is a potential theft situation, then the security company will contact a key holding company, which will send a security officer, often accompanied by a dog, to the site to intercept or deter the thieves. Once on-site, the security officer will call the police if necessary or report back to the CCTV monitoring company.

Having all of this in place, however, does not prevent theft incidents on solar farms. In the UK alone each year there are dozens of break-ins with few convictions. The thieves are after the copper in the cable, which they can sell for scrap quickly and in an untraceable manner. Thieves sometimes steal modules, but they are harder to dismount under time pressure and more difficult to sell. Most thefts happen at night, not only to avoid being caught but to avoid electrocution. Thieves cut through potentially live cables with little to no awareness of the risk to their lives; modern solar farms therefore must have the most sophisticated CCTV and security systems, and they must practise and test their scenario or incident response protocol and procedures. An efficient, well-rehearsed procedure will significantly increase the chances of theft prevention or interruption.

Meteorological equipment

Meteorological equipment is critical on a solar installation as the power generated on any given site is directly proportional to the irradiance and temperature that the solar modules are exposed to. You can use the meteorological data to calculate what a given site should be producing; if there is a discrepancy between the actual production and the calculated theoretical production, you know there is an issue.

Apart from temperature sensors and wind gauges, the one piece of equipment which is unique to solar is called the pyranometer. This is a flying-saucer-shaped device with a clear dome which detects the irradiance levels in watts per square metre (W/m^2) units. This is the same W/m^2 value which you may have seen on irradiation maps showing light levels increasing as you get closer to the equator. Typically, you will have at least one pair of pyranometers on-site: one mounted parallel to the ground and the other mounted parallel to the inclination of the modules. Pyranometers need accurate calibration every two years, and this involves sending them away to an accredited laboratory.

Now you know what components make up a solar PV system, it's time to explore the different applications and sub-industries in solar PV in Chapter Three.

3

Solar Sectors And Applications

Solar PV's popularity has exponentially increased worldwide from around 2010 onwards. Before then, only speculative and trial systems were deployed, and only in small quantities and sizes. In the modern era, several applications and market sectors have emerged. Let's look at them one by one:

Rooftop

Domestic or residential

Domestic or residential solar refers to the installation of a small solar system on a domestic dwelling. They are typically 1 kW to 5kW in size (four to twenty modules), with small string or micro inverters.

Residential government-backed subsidies have led to significant uptake in Western countries, and they are often part of a scheme to lower consumers' private energy cost. In some cases, they also provide a green energy income when selling energy back to the local network.

Subsidies in more mature markets around the world have recently slowed down due to the reduction in solar system costs. Schemes are still available, though, and – depending on your roof's suitability for solar, your household's consumption and other factors – you can still yield immediate savings on your electricity bills and paybacks in four to eight years.

Two technological and cultural shifts are happening right now which will transform the residential solar arena. The first one is the development of domestic-scale battery storage systems, which enables you to store energy during the middle of the day (when most households don't need it) and consume this energy either when it's more expensive or when you need it in non-daylight hours. Once battery technology matures and prices come down, this will become a no-brainer for every home. The second shift relates to the inevitable migration from fossil fuel cars to electric vehicles. Within a decade, over three-quarters of all cars bought will be electric and you will need to charge your vehicle at home. There are a range of fantastic, fast-charging products out there which integrate into your solar and battery storage systems and charge your car in the most efficient and cost-effective way.

Solar slates and tiles

On domestic, solar slates and tiles seem to be one of the starting points for the Internet of Things (IoT).[10] There are predictions that you'll be able to use the fully charged vehicle sitting on your drive as a form of battery storage or an electricity generation device and sell power back to the network while you sleep. This may domino into more industrial- or commercial-scale schemes, with fleets of electric pool vehicles at depots or facilities feeding energy or balancing frequencies on the network on a larger scale.

With this in mind, I feel we should legislate installing solar PV on all new-build properties. We are in a climate emergency, and buildings need roofs anyway, often with access equipment. A solar PV system would reduce the homeowner's carbon footprint, lower their bills and support the wider Net-Zero carbon goals.

Traditional retrofitted solar panels on a roof may soon be a thing of the past as companies bring to market a fully integrated solar roof system – a power generation solution which covers your entire roof. Tesla, as the market leader, claims that their solar roof slates are three times stronger than traditional slate or ceramic tiles and have a lifetime guarantee.[11] Their goal is to make them for the same cost as traditional slate or tile equivalents, though they are not yet capable of this today. If you are looking to reroof your property, fancy solar on your roof and have to pay for access equipment anyway, this might be worth considering. Solar slates, along with integrated battery storage and electric vehicle (EV) charging capability, will be rapidly rolled out over the next few years, so keep an eye out for this growth market taking off.

Commercial and industrial scale

The commercial and industrial solar market is its own subsector and refers to any commercial or industrial installation. Typically commercial and industrial solar is installed to increase energy efficiencies, lower and secure energy bills, and take advantage of the large roof spaces – in most cases to mount solar PV. I feel this area has the most potential for easy gains with PV adoption in the UK. There is an estimated 250,000 hectares of south-facing commercial roof space in the UK. If used, this could provide approximately 50% of the UK's electricity demand.[12] I predict that at some stage, developers will be legally required to integrate renewable energy into all new-build commercial and industrial premises.

Large-scale and utility

'Large-scale' – or 'utility-scale', depending on where you are – refers to ground mount systems of a certain size which are connected to the distribution network or national grid. For UK regulators, 'large-scale' refers to any site over 5MWp, but I would class a 1MWp site as large-scale.

In the UK, as of Q1 2021 there is over 8GWp (gigawatt peak) of large-scale capacity (sites over 5MWp in installed capacity), all connected to the distribution network via approximately 1,250 individual sites. On a worldwide basis, at the end of 2019 it was estimated that there were over 629GWp of solar installed, 60% of which was deployed in Asia, 16% in Europe, 12% North America and 12% in the rest of the world. Globally, that's a staggering half a billion solar modules, over half of which are installed on utility-scale assets.[13]

I will touch on how a large-scale solar farm is set up and who the main players are later in the book. For now, it is safe to say that the majority of these large-scale solar farms are owned by energy funds, large financial institutions, and fund and asset management companies who raise capital from investors with the promise of over twenty-five years' worth of consistent, mature-technology-generated returns.

The other thing to highlight about large-scale relates to the way that the asset is cared for once it's operational. Since a large-scale ground mount is such an expensive and lucrative asset, it needs to perform well, have high levels of reliability and, as designed, needs to last for the projected project life cycle of twenty-five years plus. These requirements justify a focus on decent levels of O&M. O&M markets spring up in all new regions of solar deployment; they start off region specific but end up consolidating, with the service price point falling until a high-quality service cannot be provided. This is what happened in Germany, Spain, Italy and the UK.

Off-grid and stand-alone systems

All over the world there are domestic, industrial and, in some cases, utility-scale needs and opportunities to establish complete off-grid solutions. These solutions provide power generation via renewables (wind, solar or other) and this power is consumed or stored in an energy-saving device so it's available when it's needed.

Rising energy prices make energy independence a sensible choice, whether at your home – installing a few solar panels, or having a battery storage unit and an EV charge point on your house – or scaling this up to your business or community. With the right engineering solution, it's possible to create power systems which are not connected to the power grid or distribution system.

This also works in communities which are isolated from the distribution network or when it's just too expensive to set up the heavy electrical infrastructure needed to connect and sell energy on the merchant market. In these cases, island power stations can be developed. Other community-based solutions include WiFi stations, clean water purification and production, shelter, crop management and charging for EVs. This is an area which I am excited about for the future. This technology is available now, and – with the right funding and project support – it can help thousands, if not millions, around the world.

I also predict that in more developed countries, due to distribution network constraints and limitations of network investments, there will be a growing need for 100% mobile power solutions. These solutions could power a wide range of events and industrial applications, much like diesel generators do today. Their capacity will also extend to local communities and may include EV charging stations. The challenge remains to make them 100% renewable, but I'm sure this will be achieved over the coming years.

Floating solar

Floating solar has become increasingly popular over the last few years. Such systems use lakes, reservoirs, dams and water bodies, which would otherwise have no practical use, and in some applications, they reduce water evaporation rates, which aids water applications and retention.

Floating solar consists of a floating modular pontoon system as a mounting structure which enables the modules to be anchored and angled at the optimum inclination. Pontoon and module sections are constructed on land and then connected into rows of pontoon sections. They are then floated into the water, one row at a time, until the whole system is buoyant. Floating systems are typically then fixed into a set position within a water body. Walkways built into the design of the pontoon system provide access to them.

There are three major challenges operators face with floating solar systems. Firstly, they are electrical systems floating on water, so the need to avoid contact with water makes electrical safety a bigger concern than for roof or ground mount systems. Secondly, floating solar requires systems, procedures and specialist equipment to minimise the risks of personnel falling into the water. Finally, the most disruptive challenge from a maintainability and production impact perspective is birds nesting and bird drop-pings. Water bodies suitable for floating solar systems are often popular with native and migrant birds, and the warm, sheltered solar module structures located away from any prey are perfect for birds to nest and breed in. Unfortunately, this results in lots of bird droppings, and cleaning up the mess directly affects the production of the plant and becomes an expensive and regular task. Bird nests also need to be removed periodically from the structure.

Floating solar installations have their place and some owners will continue to deploy them. Owners should ensure that the maintenance of the system is well thought through, as well as investing in bird deterrent technologies.

Carports

Carport systems, like floating solar, are deployed with a dual purpose. They are typically steel or wooden structures with solar modules mounted on top, and they provide shelter from sun and rain for vehicles parked underneath.

These systems are often installed in existing car parks, so car port designers should incorporate the car parking design (usually toe to toe for efficiency) into the mounting structure design. Generally, they are either single array (usually south facing) or in an east/west arrangement if cars are parked toe to toe.

As the automobile industry transitions to electric vehicles, car ports are often futureproofed by being fitted with EV charge points so that owners can charge their parked cars while away from them.

Buildings and facades

Over the last decade, solar PV technology has become a more cost-effective option for the facades of buildings and become better suited to vertical and nonstandard applications. These PV materials must not only generate a substantial amount of renewable energy; they also need to be aesthetically attractive while complying with all relevant building materials standards.

PV facades are growing in popularity in high-rise buildings as well as in domestic and industrial applications. In some cases, they can also provide shade for the building or space, and in these cases the PV solutions are incorporated into building HVAC systems.

Transportation

You may have seen specialist demonstration cars, trains, boats or planes covered in solar PV. Currently, in the combined technology development of PV and batteries, there is a limit as to how much power PV can generate on these vehicles, and most applications still require batteries, charging or some other power source or engine. To power a typical car with 100% PV technology as it exists today, we would need so much PV that we couldn't fit down a standard street, and we'd be out of luck when it's dark. Therefore, we will always need hybrid solutions. While there are opportunities to incorporate PV on trains and ships, which will significantly lower their carbon footprint, capacity will always be the limiting factor.

Tesla, the electric vehicle giant, has hinted at integrating PV into the roof of their EV range in the future. Currently, though, the cost may outweigh the benefit, and the main driver would be aesthetics and novelty factor, as opposed to a performance enhancement or step change in their green credentials.[14]

Space applications

Solar PV in its early years was intended as a reliable power supply for space applications, potentially including the International Space Station and satellites being launched into the Earth's orbit. The space race in the 1960s benefited the international solar PV industry, accelerating the technology developments which catapulted it forward in a short space of time. With this said, it still took almost half a century for the technology to mature and scale into the principal renewable energy source on the planet.

With SpaceX, the space transportation company headed by Elon Musk, making strides into reusable space travel rockets, the race for space tourism commercialisation is well and truly underway. There are suggestions that moon and Mars colonisation is not only possible but likely within the next couple of decades. What role will PV take in these pioneering ventures? From an engineer's perspective, I have always marvelled at the proposition of having solar PV on the moon. This could provide unrivalled irradiation levels – possibly 24-hour sunlight. For moon colonisation, PV is a vital energy generation solution, since there is no option to transport combustible fuels to the moon and wind power is out of the question. There may be applications to produce hydrogen on the moon, and even biogas sources from human waste once we have suitable lunar colonisation, but solar is the likely first choice.

Conceptual designs also exist for large solar sails which are elevated to the upper realms of the atmosphere and could provide reliable renewable power without being subject to weather or limitations with ground mount systems.[15] Could the moon become a giant charging satellite, and could space travel become viable enough to transport super-efficient batteries between the moon and Earth? If green hydrogen was the fuel and if we could generate enough power, perhaps!

What is clear is that solar PV in all of its applications is making strides to better the world. Whether at a small or large scale, we are all pulling in the same direction: towards a Net-Zero future.

Now we understand the different components of a solar system and the different scales and applications, the next chapter will focus on the utility-scale sector and explore who's who within the industry.

4

Who's Who In The Solar Industry

There are several main players in the large-scale solar industry.[16] I'm not talking about individuals here, but rather what type of organisations and stakeholders are involved in the whole solar industry value chain.

It's surprising how many companies that I speak to who are involved in this value chain but are not aware of all the moving parts in solar farm development, construction, operations and beyond. This chapter outlines the key roles in the large-scale solar industry and how they relate to each other in the value chain.

So, who's first?

Developers

A solar developer is an organisation that searches for land which is suitable to receive a solar farm, considering its geographic location, irradiance levels, topology and other factors. The land must have a possible grid connection nearby (typically 11kV or 33kV), must not be an area of outstanding beauty or of archaeological interest, and its landowner must be interested in hosting a solar farm on their land.

Developers generally have an arrangement with a solar fund, which either funds or subsidises the upfront development costs, and an agreement in place regarding the stage when the developer will sell on the project (eg shovel ready or post construction).

Once developers find suitable sites, they need to conduct surveys and perform pre-design activities involving specialist consultants and advisers before they can submit a planning application to the local authority. They will present a range of planning studies, including visual impact, ecological, archaeological, flood risk and landscape, and initial pre-engineered layout plans as part of the planning application, all defining measures that the project will employ to satisfy the planning requirements and get the project over the line. They may have multiple sites going through planning at any one time. They also need to submit a connection application to the DNO. Once they have planning consent and a connection agreement in place, the last piece of the puzzle to becoming shovel ready is forming a lease agreement with the landowner.

Many developers have evolved into independent power producers (IPPs). IPPs are unlike investment funds. They develop, construct and operate power-generating assets from conception to decommissioning. They may develop and sell a small proportion of their pipeline to generate cash to feed back into the process, but their long-term aim is to establish large solar portfolios and control the quality and longevity of their assets through the whole project life cycle.

Local authorities

In the UK and other developed nations, there are local or regional authorities who control the planning process for any new development. Large-scale solar is a relatively new type of infrastructure project, and local authorities have had to learn about it on their feet to ensure that they position solar farms in suitable locations, that they will not be subject to local residence objections, and that the site will not negatively affect the aesthetics of the area, the wildlife, the plant life and even archaeological artefacts which could be buried on the land. Studies, plans and a long list of control measures are minimum requirements for planning application success.

The local authority also has to deal with the downward pressures and incentives to deploy green energy schemes from the national government – not always an easy balance to strike. In the UK, there are three words from local authorities that send shivers down developers' spines: greater crested newts. These are an endangered and protected species in the UK, and they can impact any construction development. Newts are just one of many species which can throw a spanner in the works; others include bats, badgers, birds, voles, otters and adders, and they all need protecting and conserving in the locality of the solar farm, particularly in the construction phase. As the site beds in, however, it has the potential to become an enhanced habitat for insects and small animals. As local authorities have gained experience, they've been able to move solar development through their systems quicker, and most solar developers are now aligned with their needs. The big challenge for local authorities in a post-subsidy world is the scale of the solar farms coming through. Solar farms boasting several hundred megawatts (MW) are on the horizon, and these bring larger impacts and more objections to deal with – and plenty of newts, too.

Landowners

Historically, the majority of landowners have been farmers, and many UK farmers have been willing to diversify their agricultural businesses into renewables and reap the financial benefits.

As developers arrange lease agreements with the landowners, the solar asset itself does not belong to the landowner, and the project owner will pay a type of rent to the landowner – a price per acre or hectare per year – for use of their land (typically through a special purpose vehicle or SPV). I have seen prices ranging from £500 to £1,000 per acre per year, meaning that a 5MWp site, which is traditionally approximately 25 acres, would return the landowner between £12,500 and £25,000, which is a pretty good deal when compared to any agricultural crop yield comparison.

The other sweetener that you often find in these arrangements is that the farmer will be tied into the ongoing grounds maintenance of the site, either through the O&M contractor or direct from the asset owner. This typically includes grass management, hedge trimming and tree maintenance. The other option, which has become popular for ecological, land use justification and economic reasons, is to have sheep grazing on the site.

District network operators

A district network operator (DNO) is responsible for the distribution network within their regional area. The DNOs manage, balance, maintain and operate these networks in conjunction with National Grid, who are responsible for the higher-rated transmission network. Few solar projects are connected directly to grid, so let's focus on the DNOs.

In the UK, there are six DNOs:[17]

- Western Power Distribution

- Scottish and Southern Energy

- UK Power Networks

- ScottishPower Energy Networks

- Northern Powergrid

- Electricity North West Limited

Each group is responsible for managing new power generation projects on their turf. For new-build solar projects, which require new connections and in some cases infrastructure upgrades, DNOs are usually involved. A DNO would receive a connection application from a developer requesting an export capacity and import capacity and providing details of the nature of the power generation asset. The DNO must then provide a connection offer, which usually consists of two parts.

The first part is 'non-contestable' works, which the DNO will need to do themselves because they involve direct contact, isolation or interaction with the network. The second part is the 'contestable' works.

For these works, the DNO provides an offer – usually subcontracted to a preferred and approved independent connection provider (ICP). However, as this is the contestable element, project developers are free to engage with their own preferred ICP or go to market in a competitive arena.

Although DNOs perform critical work, they are historically inflexible, slow to respond and have often caused project delays, even occasionally causing projects to miss subsidy deadlines. This is because they need to respond in a consistent and considered way for each application. It would be helpful if they could provide informal guidance as to likely export capacity threshold points for proposed projects before formal connection applications are made. This would save many wasted applications and precious time for projects that are not viable. It would also be helpful if the connection for a 10MWp farm, for example, would cost £250,000 and use the existing connection infrastructure, but an 11MWp connection would cost £1.2 million, as significant infrastructure upgrades are required. If you put in an application for the 11MWp scheme, then they wouldn't tell you that if you reduced this by 1MWp, you would make these substantial savings. I know why they do it, as they can't provide a tailored service for everyone, but for me this is short-sighted and squandering opportunities to optimise their networks. However, most DNOs are implementing events and initiatives to improve their communication and performance and streamline their processes. Let's hope these improvements continue to be implemented.

In some nations, the distribution network is run like a monopoly (with a single government-owned operator), and a combination of lack of experience, ignorance and occasionally even corruption is a challenge for utility-scale solar deployment. The UK went through this transition with solar a decade ago, but now has learnt to listen to sector experts and to work with the market as it evolves. Without naming specific nations, my limited exposure to two or three other markets close to the UK has felt like stepping back in time with regards to dealing with the network operators. These nations need to learn quickly from boom-and-bust cycles, understand what works and what doesn't, and remove the shackles to maximise solar PV deployment. In the UK, we can count ourselves lucky, as having six regional DNOs does work, although there is room for improvement. In Germany, by contrast, there are over 800 distribution grid operators![18]

ICPs

Independent connection providers (ICPs) are historically electrical or power engineering companies who, through a process of approvals and authorisations, can provide connection services and solutions to the DNO or in association with a DNO connection project. In most cases for a solar project, the project developer, owner, or even the engineering, procurement and construction (EPC) contractor engages them to conduct the contestable element of the DNO connection offer – generally the design and construction of the on-site substation (including transformers, switchgear, relays and protection equipment). They often conduct the site-to-DNO substation cabling as well, which may be kilometres away from the site.

My experiences with ICPs were largely negative during the UK solar boom. Some individuals shone through as experts and really delivered, but the sector was riddled with over-stretched, poorly organised and poorly communicated projects, which caused delays and missed subsidy deadlines.

In my previous roles, where we had experienced this chaos first-hand, we always recommended that the EPC company invest in a DNO or ICP coordinator role. This person would be an HV or connections expert who could keep the DNO and ICP on track, push them to stick to their programmes and make sure they don't forget to order parts. With the projects that had a DNO or ICP coordinator, there were no issues, and we saved time and money.

EPCs

'EPC' stands for 'engineering, procurement and construction'; it is a term used in the title of the principal contractor who builds the solar asset. As the name suggests, they are traditionally responsible for engineering the asset, procuring the components and constructing the system itself.

Typically, either the developer or the solar fund who has purchased the project from the developer will be looking for an EPC to build their farm(s). These companies are usually large, have a strong balance sheet and can bankroll at least the front half of any given project. There may be a partnership in place, meaning that a specific EPC will build out all of a portfolio, or there may be competitive tenders where the EPC will need to compete on cost, design, health and safety management, historic performance and programme.

EPC prices have tumbled over the last few years (the biggest impact being the price of solar modules), and solar is now the energy system with the cheapest levelised cost of energy (LCOE) in the world. Solar farms are now being built below £500,000/MWp – a number which continues to fall – and the pressure is on EPCs to build these assets quickly, efficiently and without fuss, and ensure they last their twenty-five-year design life.[19]

Pure-play EPCs typically roam the planet looking for emerging solar markets. In Europe this trend started in Spain, Italy and Germany, then it migrated over to the UK between 2011 and 2016, and it's now present in Australia, Chile, Argentina and India. These new markets develop predominantly because of government subsidies, which lead to solar asset boom markets where every man and his dog piles in.

These boom-and-bust cycles are repetitive. Governments subsidise solar, solar is deployed beyond government predictions, governments can no longer afford to support the subsidies and remove them, and construction dries up. This happened in the UK and several other mature markets. However, the unprecedented international adoption of solar has brought tumbling module prices, and we are now staring down the barrel of a subsidy-free wave of new builds. In the UK, this wave is already underway with several hundred MWs of projects under development and construction starting in 2021.

Despite low module prices, developers and EPCs must work harder than ever to make their margins and provide financially viable projects. They must consider developments in technology such as bifacial modules, the progression of design and adoption of trackers to optimise the output profile of a given site. They must also account for the adoption of energy storage technologies to balance the grid and export at high points of demand. Finally, they must implement lessons learnt from the first solar boom in terms of construction quality assurance and risk reduction methods. They now know that asset owners will retain bonds and retentions due to punch-list issues and shortfalls in quality. If they use these lessons and apply improvements, these elements will catapult solar faster and further worldwide.

The EPC will build an asset and then be on the hook for performance and availability for at least the first two years – known as the warranty period. If the EPC has their own O&M capabilities, they will manage the asset during this period; otherwise, they will subcontract this requirement to a pure-play O&M.

O&Ms

O&M (operations and maintenance) contractors look after the solar assets once they are built. Their scope usually includes regular visual inspections, electrical testing, production and security monitoring, reporting, grounds maintenance and module cleaning.

They initially deliver an O&M contract for the warranty period or PAC-to-FAC period. The owner of the site will provide a PAC (Provisional Acceptance Certificate) when the site is fully constructed and has passed a series of performance tests. A technical adviser usually produces a punch-list or snag-list which needs to be addressed and signed off to enable the EPC to obtain PAC. Following this, there is often a two-year period before the EPC receives FAC (Final Acceptance Certificate). This is the site's final sign-off for construction quality and performance. O&M contractors aim to secure the contract for multiple years after FAC, once the EPC has stepped out of contract.

In maturing solar O&M markets, we have witnessed significant service price reductions and major consolidation. Rather than a portfolio owner having ten to fifteen O&M contractors, once their sites achieve FAC they tender for two to three preferred O&M specialists. In the UK, over the last two to three years, this process has pushed out smaller independent O&M companies, who have either had to diversify or step out of the second-tier O&M sector altogether, as owners prefer the risk profile of the larger established organisations. Unless you are a 'bankable' O&M, then you are wasting your time. This essentially means you need either a big European-based, fund-backed parent company, or you need to be of a substantial size, managing several hundred MWs of solar, usually achieved through mergers and acquisitions. This is a challenging space for smaller, up-and-coming O&M companies, regardless of how good they are or what services they offer.

During the UK boom (2011–2016) prices started off in the range of £10,000–£20,000 per MWp per year. In 2021, prices are in the range of £4,000–£6,000 per MWp per year. O&Ms can only swallow this reduction if they have scale. For O&M companies to be sustainably profitable at these price ranges, they need hundreds of MWp. With scale comes complexity, though, and large-portfolio O&M is as much about logistical planning as it is about solar expertise. With congested roads, rising fuel costs, distressed assets, and pressure on response and rectification times, O&Ms face a continuous struggle to remain compliant and keep their heads above water.

At current prices, O&Ms have little room or incentive to do more than the bare minimum for owners. Fortunately, advancing technologies and approaches are starting to enable O&Ms to add more value. Services such as high-volume electroluminescence (EL) surveys, mobile lab testing (EL/Flash), thermography assessments, optimisation technology and shade analysis assessments can make O&Ms stand out and increase their profit margins and standing in the industry.

Asset owners and fund managers

At the time of writing this book, the UK has around 8GWs of installed capacity of utility-scale ground mount solar, spread over approximately 1,250 solar farms. These farms have seventy to eighty different owners, although three-quarters of the installed capacity belongs to the top twenty fund management companies, who have raised funds to finance the building or acquisition of solar assets.[20] Many of these funds have become solar specialists, exclusively owning and operating solar assets in the UK and elsewhere.

In the early days of the solar boom in the UK, there were a few funds that worked opportunistically, buying shovel-ready sites, funding the development of sites, or only keeping them for a couple of years before selling to make their returns before repeating or moving on to something else. However, many of the funds that accumulated multiple sites are laser focused on providing their investors the promised returns. The better the performance of the site in terms of yield and production, the bigger their cut, and in the early years being involved in the sharp end of the work face, solar funds developed a reputation of being 'bean-counters' and out of touch with the practicalities of engineering and power generation project delivery.

I'm pleased to say that recently these funds have started to invest heavily in their technical capabilities to ensure they are in an informed position to make reactive and future investment decisions for their portfolios. A few proactive funds are starting to invest in gaining deep understanding of their sites using developing advanced analytical techniques, including data analytics, AI, computer learning, module testing, EL and optimisation studies. This forward-looking approach will not only show them where they can make quick performance gains; it will maximise long-term returns and add value to their assets if they sell them on.

The elephant in the room here is the general standard of the assets in the UK fleet – and likely in other global markets too. Price- and time-driven EPCs were put under pressure to get these assets in the ground and connected by 31 March year on year, installing throughout the winter months, sometimes using cheap materials and components that are not compatible or fit for purpose. Some solar assets were installed using substandard labour with little to no technical quality control, resulting in a glut of poorly constructed sites which will never last twenty-five years. Solar funds need to get ahead of the curve here and make sure they know the true condition of their sites, not just the surface indications that EPCs and O&Ms provide. Major asset revamping and repowering is coming – and soon.

Asset managers

Asset managers are organisations working on behalf of the asset owner. They ensure that all the commercial elements of the solar farm are being managed – such as power sales, subsidy returns, OFGEM communications, corporate compliance, legals, contract and documentation management, accountancy and invoicing – and they usually have some authority over the O&M contractor on-site, making sure they complete their monthly reports and work within the scope they are being paid for, and they ensure the site is performing as it should.

These services are usually office based, and in the UK, they are often London or city-based organisations.

There are exceptions, however, and the evolving role of an asset management company now includes site-based inspections, data analytics and AI diagnostic tools to add greater value for site owners. Their focus has turned to data and gains they can make to the performance of the solar assets, which increases the pressure on EPCs and O&Ms to follow the letter of their contracts. They also offer support to asset owners in the form of strategic outcome project management on larger multi-site projects. Despite their large remit, with asset owners' internalisation of the asset management function, asset managers are under pressure to prove their worth and bring innovation and value to the table.

TAs

Technical advisers (TAs) are involved at various stages of the solar asset deployment value chain. They provide pre-design or technical studies at the development stage. They bring technical due diligence into projects, EPCs, technology selection and portfolio strategy advice, and they are the technical lead on mergers and acquisitions. From the perspective of the client engaging the TA, they are a risk reduction service, and in some cases, they are necessary to secure funding or a particular deal.

Like many consultants, TAs have historically had a poor reputation. Like lawyers, they are always on the clock, they use nonspecialist graduates to regurgitate report templates, and they are largely office based without the practical in-field experience to provide an in-depth technical assessment of a project. Plus, since we all went through this solar boom together, there were huge pressures on multiple parties to get solar projects connected and on the bars by 31 March each year; to say things were missed or glossed over is an understatement. I have conducted assessments, testing or visits at over 10% of the UK's sites over the last decade, and the condition of most of these sites is shocking – and TAs have signed off these sites.

Many of these issues still exist; however there is a new generation of TAs looking to do things differently and add value. Investing in expertise and, in my view, 'real engineers' is a step in the right direction. Add to this TAs' increasing appetite for innovation and value-adding services and solutions, and their reputation starts to change. They too, are investing in advanced analytical methods to maximise their asset knowledge and explore optimisation opportunities and site improvements, so the future is bright for evolutionary TAs.

Other organisations involved in large-scale solar

The following organisations and specialist companies are also worth mentioning in this chapter:

OFGEM

OFGEM is the UK government regulator for gas and electricity markets. Other countries have similar regulators, and they administer subsidy schemes. The UK still operates feed-in tariffs (FiTs) and renewable obligations certificates (ROCs) – two subsidy schemes designed to incentivise the solar sector. For each kilowatt hour (kWh) of green energy they produce, solar assets on these schemes generate a revenue stream in addition to power sales. In utility-scale solar in the UK, and in many other regions, the LCE has dropped enough for governments to remove subsidies, meaning that projects and generating plants are viable without them. This is a great sign for the sustainability of solar. New builds now have fewer interactions with OFGEM, but it must honour all existing subsidies for operational assets for twenty years plus.

Policymakers and politicians

Policymakers working for governments influence the utility-scale solar industry. These individuals are not necessarily experts in energy, engineering or climate change, but they develop and reform acts, regulations and guidance with the assistance of expert advisers. They feed the energy and solar PV deployment policies they create to politicians to gain support, lobby and enact these policies into law through legislative bodies.

Having spoken to multiple developers, asset owners and IPPs, I've identified three major issues that solar faces regarding the UK's law-making process. Firstly, the UK government engages with out-of-touch consultants who rely on publicly available data, which is usually twelve to eighteen months out of date and is no longer accurate. Secondly, through the consultants' ill-informed advice, the UK government created a subsidy scheme which led to a boom-and-bust scenario. This allowed developers at the time to have free rein on solar farm developments and created an unaffordable subsidy burden on the government. The point of the UK's subsidy system was to encourage solar farm construction, but the government woefully underestimated the uptake, forcing them to abruptly discontinue the subsidy scheme. Thirdly, the UK's subsidy scheme creators didn't consider the national distribution and transmission system which these solar farms would be connected to. Within five years, connection capacity dried up and the utility-scale sector now needs significant investment to expand its possibilities.

It is also worth mentioning that global solar PV adoption is massively influenced not only by the UK, but Europe, the United States and larger influential nations like China, Russia and India. It seems that the world is now aligning itself with a solar PV future.

We need reform if we want to hit our Net-Zero targets. I have compiled a list of tips for policymakers and politicians drawn from my exposure to the utility-scale solar sector and from influential experts in the field. This Top Tips list is available for download at www.2degreeskelvin.org/resources.

Insurers and brokers

Solar farms are insured with all-risk construction cover during the construction phase and then an engineering policy during the operational phase. Most companies find a suitable broker and then they go out to the market. The receipt of the premium quotations is inevitably followed by a sharp intake of breath and a feeling of nausea over the cost of suitable cover. Insurance is critical, though, and projects wouldn't go ahead without it.

Each company in the sector needs, at minimum, professional indemnity (PI) and combined liabilities insurance policies. These policies are expensive, and insurers are hesitant about providing cover to the renewable energy market because it's relatively new and because there are so many claims. Can you prove lightning struck a solar farm, or was it a short circuit fault? Have you mounted a piece of equipment designed specifically for indoor use in an outdoor panel covered by your policy? When does a plant breakdown become an insurance claim, and is business interruption covered in your policy? Insurance is a minefield, and I strongly advise working with reputable and knowledgeable professionals who will guide you on the policies you will need to sleep easy at night.

Aerial inspection specialists

Aerial inspection specialists carry out thermography, high-resolution surveys and, more recently, EL inspections via drone across entire solar farms. This information is analysed to provide a high-level overview of the operational condition of each asset. These services can also add value to new-build projects by tracking construction progress and creating aerial view records of the locations and routes of the critical electrical equipment and construction structures.

Solar cleaning specialists

Some sites require more module cleaning than others, due to bird droppings, dust, dirt, pollen, lichen and other substances which obscure light from getting through to the PV surface, reducing the site's performance. Many module cleaning specialists started off as general cleaning companies that turned their hands to cleaning solar modules rather than windows. They used the same equipment and – to ensure they didn't invalidate the module warranties – they needed to use filtered deionised water. In the early days, teams of operatives would manually clean modules with carbon fibre poles and brushes, but they soon realised that although cleanliness levels were good, the price, time and human effort required to clean multi-MW sites were excessive. To combat these costs, specialist machinery and even robots were designed and brought on to the market. Nowadays, specialist companies use power brushes with long, rotating, cylindrical brush heads, usually attached to a tractor. These brushes can clean multi-MW sites faster and cheaper without damaging the modules.

Grounds maintenance specialists

Grounds maintenance specialists have emerged within the sector, predominantly to avoid shading losses on solar farms but also to keep grass and vegetation levels down. These specialists have developed solar-farm-specific equipment and methods to keep solar farms trim, eliminating the practical difficulties of cutting grass under the arrays by reaching underneath the leading edge of the modules. They also use robotic grass cutters directly underneath the arrays to drive through in between vertical steelwork. These companies may also be responsible for planting saplings and hedges, sowing grass and flower seed mixes, or levelling or preparing the grounds on a solar farm.

Technology suppliers and developers

The term 'technology developers' encompasses technology companies that develop equipment specifically for the solar sector – to either improve a process or improve the performance of a solar farm. Such equipment could include the main components, such as modules, inverters or mounting structure; innovative and niche technology, such as equipment to reverse solar module deterioration, optimise modules and strings, or test modules and strings; or digital tools, which are moving into AI-driven predictive maintenance and performance optimisation. In many of these cases, manufacturers also use distributors to sell their products. These distributors and wholesalers stock the products and are educated on their features and attributes before selling directly to installers.

Renewable sector recruitment agencies

Recruitment agencies don't have the best reputation in most sectors. For many years in my own career, I saw recruitment agencies as an expense that I could (and should) avoid. However, I've learnt that people are the heart of a business and – particularly in a specialist sector such as large-scale solar – a specialist agent is worth their weight in gold. I recommend finding an agent that specialises in solar, not just in recruitment.

HV specialists

HV (high-voltage) specialists have developed a micro-niche as traditional O&M companies would include expensive, experienced HV experts in their initial teams. Unless there is scale, they cannot justify a full-time in-house HV expert, so why not subcontract the function? HV experts usually pick up all the HV side of the O&M scope, and they have more rigorous health and safety and electrical safety rules. After all, they are handling electrical systems that would vaporise you if you got it wrong.

Where does 2DK fit in?

The 2DegreesKelvin team and I are proud that we don't fit into any of these categories. We exist to support the entire solar industry and project life cycle with specialist services and solutions. We have designed a business and our own niche in the market which hasn't existed before. We describe ourselves as the grout between the tiles, a Swiss army knife or utility tool which is flexible, adaptable and dependable. Create your own niche and perform well in it.

Roles within utility-scale solar organisations

As well as understanding the types of organisations in the utility-scale solar industry, it's also useful to know what sort of roles exist in each of these organisations. Table 1.1 provides a list of role titles and types of organisations they may work for. It isn't an exhaustive list as there will be many variations to the traditional functional roles (administration, HR, directors, etc); however, it can be a useful resource for those looking to join the solar or renewable sector or to help individuals already in the industry broaden their awareness.

Role titles and organisation types

Role Title	Developers	TAs	EPCs	Asset Owners and Managers	O&M	Others
Project Developer	x					
Investment Manager				x		
Asset Manager				x		
Performance Analyst		x		x	x	
Project Manager	x	x	x	x	x	x
Site Manager			x		x	
Supervisor			x		x	
Engineer	x	x	x	x	x	x
Designer	x	x	x			
Installer			x		x	
O&M Manager					x	

Role Title	Developers	TAs	EPCs	Asset Owners and Managers	O&M	Others
O&M Coordinator					x	
Authorising Engineer			x		x	x
Authorised Person (AP)			x		x	x
Senior Authorised Person (SAP)			x		x	x
Field Service Technician					x	
UAV Pilot					x	x
Engineering Consultant	x	x	x	x	x	x
Planning Consultant	x					
Quality Manager			x			x
Health & Safety Adviser		x	x		x	x
Module Cleaning Operative					x	
Grounds Maintenance Operative					x	

Within each of these roles, there are levels, such as graduate or senior, and you may find regional representatives (eg Senior Solar Technician, South West O&M Manager, Graduate Solar Engineer).

5

The Competency Gap

In this chapter, I want to discuss the need for the solar industry to professionalise itself faster. When the solar boom took place, the driving force in terms of knowledge and understanding of solar design, construction methods and O&M standards came from more mature markets such as Germany, Spain and Italy. The UK adhered to their standards, procedures, systems and – to a large extent – pricing norms. While electrical standards may not be significantly lower in these countries than in the UK, they are a lot more relaxed. This includes what we would deem high-risk tasks such as switching, electrical testing and construction methods, as well as general levels of competency. On several occasions, I have witnessed individuals who don't have suitable training and competencies performing high-risk tasks in a casual and unprofessional manner. The industry has been lucky that there have not been more serious injuries or even deaths relating to this competency gap.

Having transitioned in my career from heavy industry in oil refineries and power stations, I have also noticed that standards in solar farm design, construction and operations are significantly lower from a health and safety and process safety perspective. Solar is a simpler system, with only a handful of electrical subsystems and static components, but it is essentially a power station, so my belief has always been to treat it that way. The immaturity of the electrical safety systems is compounded by the low competency levels of individuals coming into the solar market. This is not these individuals' fault – they want to enter the renewables market for the greater good and to possibly further their careers. It's the market, which has been in a rush to deploy solar at pace, that is to blame. Solar PV needs to drag itself through its electrical safety and competency adolescence and, as a parent would tell a grumpy and confused teenager, 'grow up'.

What this competency gap exposes is the fact that there is no solar-specific qualification which provides professionals in the solar industry with a nationally recognised proof of competency. In fact, we need more than a single qualification to be deemed as competent. We need a competency framework, covering not only the technical aspects of solar development, design, construction, commissioning, operation and mainte-nance, but also covering bespoke and other relevant elements such as health and safety; environmental, social and corporate governance; quality; values; behaviour; compliance; and leadership and manage-ment. Competency is made up of knowledge, ability, training and experience, or the acronym KATE.[21] You can't just skip to the experience part. If we can create a 360-degree approach together with a management portal to build a competent workforce that doesn't rely on a company induction and buddying up with a more experienced operative, then we can make serious progress.

The UK has formal electrical qualifications, such as the Institution of Engineering and Technology's 18th Edition Wiring Regulations and City & Guilds Inspec-tion and Testing, but these only touch on solar and working with DC systems. They are focused on elec-trical systems in general, not specifically PV. There are also solar microgeneration-scheme-related courses which are pitched at installers for residential system installation, but there's nothing for the utility-scale sector.

Everyone in the utility-scale solar industry is after great people. Great people sometimes need to come from other industries, and they need academic and practical training to bring them up to the minimum acceptable standard. If we want to achieve world decarbonisation and the unprecedented adoption of solar, where will we find the solar professionals to deliver this transition? Not only that, but as well as the design, development, construction, commissioning, O&M roles (which are in massive demand now), as the world evolves, other specialist skills and roles are emerging, such as cyber security, energy traders and information technology experts.

With this question in mind, and with the intention of imparting knowledge on a fast-growing utility-scale sector, 2DegreesKelvin have designed a range of utility-scale solar training courses which provide training in an online environment together with on-site training where required. We developed resources that individuals can use to standardise and professionalise certain roles and encourage amazing people to develop their careers in this rapid-growth industry. These courses are for people and organisations worldwide who appreciate UK standards and training levels and who want their growing teams to have a strong foundation in utility-scale solar PV and the end-to-end process.

Currently, the biggest demand in terms of roles in the utility solar sector seems to be for field service technicians – a common, long-term and growing role within O&M organisations. I would argue that this role is one of the easiest to get into as organisations will consider you if you are partially electrically qualified; in many cases, you don't need any solar experience or solar-specific qualifications. However, due to the general lack of solar and DC system competence and the fact that the role exposes the operative to electrically hazardous environments on a daily basis, I would suggest that this area needs the greatest focus. The 2DegreesKelvin training and competency solutions are centred around these types of hands-on roles in which operatives expose themselves to life-threatening hazards. You're not going to get electrocuted by DC from your office desk.

Even if your company is involved in this industry but has no physical contact with anything on a solar farm – your roles are more administrative, commercial, financial, sales or management – it is useful for your entire team to have a foundation in solar PV, from the technology to the development process, to the construction and O&M process. This gives your team context as to where they as individuals, your organisation and your products or services fit into the market.

Training and competency for any role within the solar PV industry is available from 2DegreesKelvin:

www.2degreeskelvin.org. Also, my second book will provide utility-scale solar organisations with the processes and tools they need to develop world-class solar professionals. To find out more, go to www.2degreeskelvin.org/training.

PART TWO

PV ASSETS

Part Two of this book looks at solar's past and its present. Chapter Six focuses on operational solar farms, most of which were built during the solar boom. It explores who the key players are in the operational phase of a solar farm and how they interact with each other. Drawing on knowledge I gained from visiting over 10% of the 8GW utility-scale fleet in the UK, I share my insights and expose some of the shortfalls in quality control and installation standards which were an inevitable consequence of the boom.

As operational assets are ageing, advanced testing and inspection methods have evolved and been brought to market. Chapter Seven analyses the pros and cons of these methods and how they can be adopted to maximise asset knowledge and performance.

Unfortunately, the writing is on the wall for the UK solar fleet, as may be the case in other countries that have experienced solar booms. These assets will not last twenty-five years without significant intervention. In Chapter Seven, we also explore module warranty claims, site optimisation and the road to repower, all of which demand a new breed of specialist service provider to bring sick assets back to life.

Chapters Eight and Nine focus on new-build assets. These chapters come after the ones on operational assets because you need to know what was built before, and the operational consequences, to understand what lessons to apply for the new-build pipeline. Let's get the balance and priorities right this time when it comes to pitching capital expenditure (CAPEX) versus operational expenditure (OPEX). Let's emphasise accurate design simulations, construction quality management, and proactive module testing to minimise the chance of introducing defects on day one and maximise performance and longevity. Let's propel solar PV to the top of the energy champions league!

6

Operational Assets –
Fleet Status

L ooking at the UK utility-scale fleet, as of Q3 2021 the average age of the assets is just under seven years old. This is compared to similar solar booms that occurred in Spain, Germany and Italy approximately two years earlier than in the UK: these more mature European markets' average asset is approaching nine years old. It's clear from the uptrend in revamping and repowering projects that the pre-ten-year-old mark is a tipping point for system health in a substantial proportion of operational fleets around the world. In fact, lack of quality control on the manufacturing of modules, cabling, inverters and HV equipment, combined with shortcuts made during the construction of these subsidy-fuelled assets, point towards big decision points on the horizon for asset owners.

But before we get ahead of ourselves, it's important to understand some context. During the operational phase of any solar farm, who plays the main roles? What is the typical contractual dynamic and who is under the most pressure?

Operational phase – key players

In a typical solar farm in the UK today, who's involved in the operation, upkeep and ensuring that the cash register is ticking over? With the exception of owner-ship handover periods or a milestone (such as preliminary or final acceptance where a TA is involved), there are just three main players: the asset owner, the asset manager and the O&M company.

Asset owners

Traditionally, the asset owner is an investment fund that raises capital to develop portfolios of solar farms. These funds provide handsome returns and dividends for their investors. Asset owners play a pivotal role, not only in realising the funds necessary to deploy large-scale solar but also as decision makers in the role structure. Although asset managers and TAs counsel them, asset owners pull the trigger on decisions which affect the quality, reliability and longevity of the assets they own. If they scrimp and save, services will struggle to provide excellence down the chain.

Asset Owner

Asset Manager

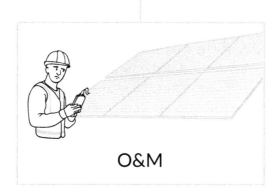

O&M

Asset owners, as entities, have evolved over the last decade. Many started off as blinkered and ignorant players in the game of solar PV, focused predominantly on the bottom line and outsourcing everything, especially technical solar knowhow. Today, although there are still many old-school asset owners who are happy with an arm's-length involvement in their assets and watch the lucrative returns flow into their pension funds, smart asset owners are investing in knowledge, expertise and teams who know how to maximise their assets' performance. In recent years, some asset owners have developed their own asset management division or subsidiary to keep the expertise in-house. For me this makes sense, although it elbows out the independent asset management companies.

Asset managers

Asset managers are often intermediaries. Their role and scope varies, but the asset owner employs them to ensure that the plant is being operated and maintained effectively, that energy and subsidy revenues are collected, and that the asset owner is legally and contractually compliant. They are an insurance policy for asset owners to keep shareholders happy.

As with other key players, not all asset managers are the same. Often, the first ones to scale in the market have the cash to invest in resources and technology.

I am aware of asset management companies who manage multiple GWs of assets for multiple asset owners all over the world; they have established mature, technically strong and innovative teams, with data-led technologies and analytical capabilities, and they provide great value to asset owners. There are also 'boutique' asset management companies that are more hands on. They go to sites, conducting investigations, carrying out tests, and pushing for site improvements and optimisation. These types of asset manager pay dividends as assets age and start failing.

Asset managers, however, are the bane of most O&Ms' lives. They get paid to poke the O&M and make sure they are fulfilling their scope of work and doing everything right. In many cases in this evolving industry, this policing is completely justified, as O&Ms struggle to keep up with their preventive and corrective maintenance obligations. With some asset owners contemplating bringing asset management in-house, the pressure is on for asset managers to justify their existence, so they need to get results. The low-hanging fruit in most cases is picking apart an O&M company and showing the asset owner what they are doing wrong. I feel that asset managers need to evolve and innovate – not only incorporating data analytics, machine learning and AI systems, but also being proactive in conducting hands-on investigations to maximise asset knowledge and in driving improvement and optimisation options as assets age.

O&M companies

Full disclosure here: I ran an O&M company for seven years, and I felt the downward technical, commercial and contractual pressures placed on them. O&Ms, unfortunately, are at the bottom of the pile contractually. The industry needs to realise that it's short-sighted to squeeze the little guy. Doing so can prevent your asset from being maintained to a suitable standard, and it wastes so much time and money on contractual discussions and issues over the years that companies could have avoided if they adopted a partnership approach.

The dynamic between O&Ms and asset owners and managers could have been different if solar farms were designed and constructed to a higher standard and operability was considered. An O&M often inherits a poorly designed and constructed site, is only paid to do basic maintenance and then is criticised for the site's lacklustre performance. If O&Ms are given well-designed and well-constructed sites, they get better results. I should also mention that O&M scopes in traditional contracts are generic and do not consider site-specific technologies, features, components or historic performance. These scopes often come from TAs and lawyers who don't have a Scooby-Doo about how to operate and maintain a solar farm. They are full of pointless tasks and do not have enough incentives for the O&M to perform beyond the basic level. They do contain plenty of liquidated damages, though, so at least the asset owner is protected. This system needs reform if asset owners want high-performing assets long into the future.

I have taken the lessons learnt and my exposure to this structure dynamic for operational solar assets and developed a downloadable list of Top Tips at www.2degreeskelvin.org/resources. These tips provide guidance to all of the main players in the utility-scale solar industry, and, if adopted, they would create a more balanced, considered and professional industry with high-quality and high-performing solar assets.

The next section lifts the lid on concerning practices that I and the 2DegreesKelvin team have witnessed in the UK fleet of solar assets. This may not be easy reading for asset owners, but there are things we can do to consolidate our position and improve the situation in the future.

Defects, damage and dire installation standards

When you buy eggs, what's the first thing you do? You check they're not cracked. Why is that? Because you don't want to buy cracked eggs.

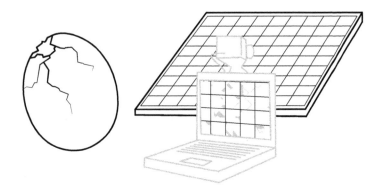

Why, then, does the UK solar industry accept broken, cracked modules that will generate future power loss for your new-build sites? Why do they ignore the fact that most operational solar fleets are riddled with defects, damage and dire installation standards? We do not ask these questions often enough.

During the UK solar boom between 2011 and 2016 the FiT and ROC subsidy regimes helped install over 8GWs of ground mount solar.[22] This was an amazing accomplishment, and the UK should be proud to lead the world in the renewable energy revolution; however, the environment was a price-driven one where cheapest was frequently best, and, due to the diminishing ROC levels every March, most construction took place in the depths of the cold and wet UK winter months. In practical and operational terms, this also meant that much of the UK fleet was constructed using substandard materials, suspect equipment selection, profit-based designs and poor installation standards. Many EPC contractors were inevitably looking for ways to cut corners, save money and maximise profits. When I speak to experts from the more mature German, Spanish and Italian markets, they confirm that this happened in their nations, and they predict it will continue to happen in emerging markets all around the world.

The main concern that I have – and that the market should have – is the primary piece of CAPEX investment contained within a solar farm: the solar modules themselves. Their origins, the fragile nature of the silicon wafer itself, manufacturing quality standards, shipping and transportation methods, the way many were thrown onto the mounting structure, and their handling during the construction phase of a plant can all damage them. All of this damage is avoidable, and therefore so are potential future losses.

Having tested over 20,000 modules and conducted site assessments on over 10% of the UK fleet, in my experience the introduction of mechanical damage to solar modules in the form of microcracks is one of the most widespread yet invisible issues on solar farms today. From our data on modules containing defects, 98% of defects are microcracks on a cell-count basis, meaning that they are by far the most prevalent cell-based defect. The other 2% encompasses everything else, including potential induced degradation (PID), soldering, grid finger interruptions, firing spots and ingot edge, to name a few.

Taking the 10% of sites in the UK that I have assessed as a representative sample, I estimate that over 75% contain significant widespread mechanical damage in the form of microcracks. These will vary in intensity, distribution and potential long-term impact. Interestingly, in most cases – and certainly in three-to-five-year-old plants – these microcracks have a negligible effect on the output power of the modules. Due to this single point on power output, most findings lead to no action. Owners then perceive advanced testing techniques such as EL and flash testing as overpriced measures that find defects with little impact on their bottom line, and which do not provide solutions, but simply point out how bad an issue they have. We need to discuss this misconception.

So, what's going on here? What is a microcrack, and, if it's not affecting production now, will it someday and by how much? How can we proactively identify microcracks in the field and address them to maximise future generation? This section of Chapter Six explores these questions.

What is a microcrack?

The terms 'microcrack' or 'microfracture' refer to fine, invisible-to-the-eye cracks in the crystalline silicon cells which make up solar modules. In most cases, the cause will be from manufacture, installation and/or operational environmental sources, and cracks will

propagate further when subjected to mechanical and /
or thermal stresses.

Although these cracks are widespread and will (at
some point) impact on cell, module or string production, they are not surprising; I believe they are inevitable. When manufacturing square cells of a brittle
material which are approximately 700 times wider
than they are thick, and then exposing them to heat,
cold, wind, rain and snow outside, microcracks are
likely. Add external forces like packing, loading,
handling and installation, and mechanical forces, and
these cracks are a foregone conclusion.

It's safe to say that module technology has advanced
significantly over the last decade, seemingly heading
towards even thinner glass thicknesses, laminate-
fronted modules, and evolving cell and busbar
designs. With the exception of a small number of
manufacturers who are heading down the thick,
strong and heavy route, and marketing with video
clips of people jumping up and down on modules to
prove their strength, the trend towards much larger
modules is introducing issues which could show
themselves in years to come as microcracks in the
field. Two-metre-plus modules now have lower snow
and wind capacities than ever before, and many in
sunnier regions in the world are mounted on tracking
systems which introduce even more dynamic forces.
We do need to pay attention to the manufacturing
methods, materials and design, but we still see

young cracks in fresh-out-of-the-box, modern-design modules and even more in the field following installation. Although the microcrack problem is not as bad as it was, it hasn't gone away. The operational fleet that has the older cell and busbar designs, which are more susceptible to microcracks, are still in use, and there are still proactive measures that we can take to further reduce microcracked modules on new-build sites.

How do microcracks affect the power output of a module?

Microcracks themselves will not cause a current flow interruption as long as the grid finger carrying the current is still intact. The grid finger is the fine, silver-compound wire which conducts the current and brings it to the thicker busbars on the solar cell. If there is a microcrack, it won't take long before the grid finger breaks. In the early stages of a recent grid finger break or tear, the current may still flow when the cell is cold and be interrupted when the cell heats up, creating a void. As the cell cycles, over time this void will widen enough to cause a current flow interruption and become permanent and irreversible.

Visualise the current being created in the blue crystalline areas of the cell and flowing to the grid fingers, and then flowing through the grid fingers to the busbars before travelling on to the next cell in series. Any interruption in these grid fingers can restrict the flow of the current and the power output of the cell and module, depending on the crack's area, orientation and length in relation to the cell.

Microcracks can create 'hot spots' on the affected cells, which can be identified using infrared thermography (IR). However, the most advanced inspection method which provides a conclusive view of the defect is electroluminescence imaging (EL). EL can reveal microcracks as fine, dark lines, usually propagating from a busbar, cell edge or impact location. Assessing them with reputable judgement criteria can lead to conclusions as to their criticality, cause and likely impact on power. Non-power-producing areas show themselves as darker or black sections of the cell under EL.

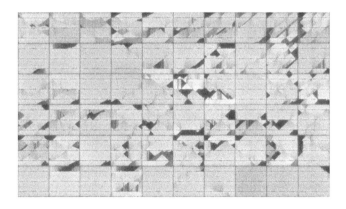

Microcracks vary in length, orientation, shape and cell location. Applying judgement criteria to the EL images on a cellular basis lets you categorise the microcracks as either 'very critical', 'critical' or 'noncritical'. Judgement criteria will have module classification thresholds for different numbers and combinations of cell defects, and these will dictate the classification of a given module. The classification will normally determine what action to take with that module (monitor, replace, escalate to test more modules, etc).

The darkness of an isolated area within a cell usually indicates the age or completeness of the crack and, in particular, the complete separation of the grid fingers; therefore, a newly cracked cell/module – even if it's classified as critical – may have little to no impact on power output. However, when the crack ages through thermal and environmental cycling and stresses, grid finger separation will worsen until they create areas of complete isolation. Each cell, batch, module and manufacturer are unique, so the cells will all deteriorate at different rates. Let's be clear, though: they will all deteriorate enough to cause significant and measurable losses in power output well within their twenty-five-year design life.

Multiple cells with losses, on multiple modules, on multiple strings will creep up on most sites, and the biggest effects will be on sites which had earlier module technology installed and where the most microcracks were introduced in their early days of construction and operation.

Methods of microcrack detection

Visual inspection

Visual inspection is one of the most under-rated inspection methods out there. Due to the scale of solar assets and the physical size of the arrays, O&Ms do not carry out visual inspections comprehensively and do not capture thorough image gathering. At best in the majority of cases, an O&M technician will walk the row looking for obvious issues. This is better than doing nothing, but a little more rigour would identify more defects. Also, as I mentioned earlier in this chapter, O&M rates are tight, and O&M technicians are often under too much pressure and not suitably trained to look thoroughly and find issues.

Although most microcracks are invisible to the human eye, it is possible to see 'snail trails'. Snail trails are believed to be caused by moisture entering the module laminate sandwich via the back sheet and making its way through to the cell itself. Then the grid finger material can dissolve, and ions migrate to the EVA (encapsulation material) and are observed on the front side of the module as either a browning discolouration on the grid fingers or small silver blobs in the middle of a darker shadowed area which resemble a snail's trail (hence the name). In many cases, the route of the snail trail follows that of a microcrack, but the two phenomena are not intrinsically linked, and one may occur without the other.

These markings appear as small dots of soldering or silver bleeding out from the grid fingers to form lines and patterns that resemble a snail's slime trail. In my experience, 'snail trails' are reasonably common, and some module manufacturers have suffered from them more than others. As they are a visible defect, many owners and asset managers want them investigated. In most cases, electrical testing and infrared (IR) thermography surveys are inconclusive; EL and flash testing, if used, confirm the microcracks, and in younger modules they detect underwhelming power losses. Many manufacturers have argued that these are a normal phenomenon and do not warrant exchange, and cases are closed on this basis. However, owners be warned: monitor these snail trails and underlying microcracks as they will affect power more as they mature.

Infrared thermography

The most popular and best bang-for-your-buck advanced inspection method to detect microcracks and other hot-spot-generating defects is IR thermography via drone. This method is widely deployed all around the world and is standard practice to gain a quick, cheap and high-level indication of module-based operational conditions. IR images are taken from the air and thermal anomalies are detected; the client usually receives them in a report or via an online portal.

There is always a balance between the minimum level of image resolution and the height, speed and subsequent cost of the given survey. This means that for off-the-shelf IR surveys, the detail visible is usually limited to:

- Disconnected strings

- Disconnected modules

- Short-circuited modules or faulty bypass diodes

- Hot spots

- Bird droppings

These anomalies generally cause either different thermal signatures (colours on the spectrum) or 'hot spots'. Hot spots can sometimes be identified by their shape and intensity of colour as bird droppings or shading, but most other thermal hot spots will need deeper investigation if the asset owner or operator wants to know exactly what they are, their likely cause and their impact on production. The other issue is that young cracks which are not generating hot spots may not be detected and will develop over time; all site owners should therefore deploy annual IR surveys and use sophisticated data presentation systems to enable year-on-year comparison, and then back these up with more advanced inspection methods to gain granular understanding.

Ultraviolet

Ultraviolet (UV) inspections are useful for identifying microcracks and indicating the age of a crack. A

UV light, preferably fitted with a specialist UV filter, is shone on to modules at night with no interaction with the solar/electrical system, and in an estimated 80% of cases (based on 2DegreesKelvin's experience) the UVA (encapsulation) ingredients emit a fluorescence effect which illuminates the healthy parts of the respective cells. Areas of the cell that have cracks form shadowed areas following the lines of the cracks; the fatter or thicker the shadow is around a given crack, the older the crack is. There have been cases where microcrack investigations carried out using UV proved that the cracks were not caused by O&M duties but were likely caused by installation.

There are trials for scaling up manual inspections using UV, using larger/longer light configurations with cameras and even drone UV. The two main issues with scaling up UV inspections are that UV inspection can only find microcracks (and nothing else) and that costs and difficulties in scaling up the volume of UV inspections will be similar to those of EL, which is a more useful method and a better ROI.

Electroluminescence

Electroluminescence (EL) is the king of all inspection methods, and its adoption is on the rise for good reason. Based on 2DegreesKelvin's and our world-leading partners' experience, EL can detect 90% of all known cell-based defects, as opposed to IR's 25%. With regards to microcracks, it provides clear images of the cracks, their orientation, length and isolated areas (and their relative darkness), and suggests areas of non-power-producing cells. Additionally, the level of detail that EL provides often enables inspectors to determine the root cause (impact points, spider cracks, cross-cracks, etc). There is a lot of research and testing going on right now to provide an intrinsic link between an EL image and the power output of a given module. This is not a simple process – it involves gathering thousands of test samples and the biggest variable is the age and completeness of the cracks which are causing the areas of isolation. Watch this space for developments in this area.

EL equipment is now widely available, including a power modulation unit (controlling amps and voltage to a given module or string) and an EL camera, which is similar to a Digital-SLR (single-lens reflex) with a modified processor and lens. Many O&M companies are now experimenting with 'point-and-shoot' methods.

2DegreesKelvin and other world leaders in this field are developing and deploying more advanced methods to gather high-quality, repeatable, perpendicular images, including tripod systems, drones and remote power sequencing technology, to maximise volume and bring the price point down. If EL costed the same as IR, we'd all use it every time, but as it involves interacting with the electrical system on a string-by-string or table-by-table basis, it is slower, requires more sophisticated and expensive equipment and trained and competent resources, and the methodology is more physically demanding, the prices matter. Currently, gathering EL images can be as cheap as £3–£5 per module with the optimum power setup. Regardless of the level of asset detail gathered and the increase in asset value for sites that are 100% EL'd, the price must continue to fall if we want mass adoption. I feel the true value of EL is still to be realised.

The use and value of in-situ EL is shifting. Over the last few years, at 2DegreesKelvin we have provided spot-check EL testing to verify PID, module damage or even for a general investigation to check if a plant is underperforming. It is reactive testing.

But, judging by the increase in enquiries, the market's understanding of EL testing use is changing, and educated owners, managers, TAs, and even EPCs and O&Ms are considering using EL testing as a proactive advanced inspection method.

EPCs and O&Ms in particular have previously seen this technology as something that they could do without – it reveals issues that they could be blamed for. However, they now understand that in-situ EL testing can fill the gap in risk management to evidence their installation and maintenance service standards, and this in turn will provide confidence to the asset owners and managers.

7

Operational Assets – Knowledge Is Power

Knowledge is power, in every sense of the word, when it comes to solar, and every watt counts. To be in an informed position regarding your assets, you need all the facts. Whether you're performing string tests, shunt resistance testing, IV-curve tests, visual inspections, IR drone surveys, or more advanced methods such as EL or flash testing, the outcome of the exercise must be justified, useful and stored in a more progressive way than traditional PDF-format reports.

2DegreesKelvin works closely with a world-leading partner who have developed a digital twin interactive portal which could soon make the PDF report a thing of the past. We take a detailed scan of the solar farm and the electrical subsystems are layered on top, as is the sequential architecture of the asset hierarchy. This enables us to hang all captured inspection data, information and images off the asset digitally. Rather than scrolling through traditional reports stored who knows where, this system provides intuitive and interactive asset-specific information in perpetuity. Its principal use case is for thermography surveys, where the IR images and anomalies are presented over the top of a site plan. You can manoeuvre your way around the site plan, click on a module and see the image that was captured. This platform enables us to upload additional information to the specific asset – IR images captured on foot, EL images, IV-curve traces or O&M inspection evidence. This is the future of asset data collection and record keeping, and hopefully it will be integrated into the solar industry as a best practice. It is important to understand that the goal isn't to revamp and repower every operational asset out there simply because there are a few issues here and there. Every asset has issues that can be rectified or improved. Many sites will continue to operate in an optimum fashion, but these have a better build quality, with better components and system designs. 2DegreesKelvin have a range of engineering services which support asset owners, O&Ms and TAs to get to a point where informed investment or strategic decisions can be made.

Much of this additional knowledge stored in advanced methods will raise alarm bells as assets age, and the dawning of the revamp and repower market is bubbling up from under the surface.

The warranty window countdown

Most solar modules have two types of warranty. Firstly, they have a performance warranty that covers the power generation of the module and follows a degradation curve or line on a graph. It may guarantee, for example, a minimum of 90% production at the ten-year stage and then a minimum of 80% production at the twenty-five-year stage. 2DegreesKelvin are frequently asked to carry out flash tests on operational modules to see where they are on this degradation curve and whether the asset owner has a performance warranty claim or not.

The second warranty is the equipment or product warranty. It generally lasts ten or twelve years, relates to the module itself, and is often limited to 'material or process defects'. Such defects can be difficult to define without looking at specific warranty details for different manufacturers, and they are usually not related to the power-producing element.

This is an important topic in the utility-scale solar industry at present as the mean age of modules in operation is now seven to ten years old. The countdown to the end of product warranty is well and truly on, so now is the time for asset owners to explore these warranties and have the modules on their solar farms inspected thoroughly to determine whether they can make a claim.

2DegreesKelvin are seeing manufacturers honouring limited product warranties in areas including PID, backsheet deterioration and delamination. Each claim requires quantitative and qualitative investigations, including on-site and lab testing to provide evidence. The outcomes of these claims have varied depending on the scale and impact of the issue. In some cases, the manufacturers have provided replacement modules, which require a module exchange program. The main issue with this outcome is that most of the power classes of modules being exchanged are no longer manufactured, so the site needs to be reconfigured and there are complications in planning to consider. We are seeing quite a bit of this now in the UK, where an agreed quantity of defect modules are removed, and are backfilled with unaffected modules on the same site – usually from one maximum power point trackers (MPPT) or inverter areas. A small number of higher-watt modules are then installed with string lengths reconfigured. This is OK for the time being, but with degenerative conditions such as PID, backsheet deterioration and delamination, there will more than likely be multiple rounds like this until all of the site's modules are replaced at some point in the future.

Other outcomes we have seen include those where the manufacturer provides compensation to the asset owner to the value of the modules purchased at the time of order, leaving it up to the asset owner to decide what to do next. Finally, in cases such as PID, the manufacturer pays for retrofittable healing technology to reverse the degradation effects, and this is deemed a suitable and sufficient solution for the asset owner. This saves time, effort and expense compared to a full exchange. There are also backseat repair or sealing approaches now being deployed, but in our view this is a short-term shoring strategy.

Although there are several positive outcomes from an asset owner's perspective, the scenarios described above do not take into consideration the dozens of failed warranty claim attempts which take place. Based on industry knowledge and feedback from some of our technical partners, we estimate that only one in ten claims is successful. The majority of failed claims are due to the watertight nature of the module manufacturers' warranties themselves; other claims fail because asset owners – or their TAs building the claim – have little practical experience or knowledge of these issues in the field. We are set for a busy few years, as the finger of blame continues to move around the room until someone pays the bill.

SOS and Road2Repower

Is my asset suitable for revamping and repowering?

2DegreesKelvin have developed a site optimisation suitability, or SOS, assessment process. Based on the site design, current condition, installation standards, historic operational performance, safety concerns and system components, our assessment provides a percentage rating on a site, which indicates its suitability for improvement, optimisation, and revamping and repowering solutions.

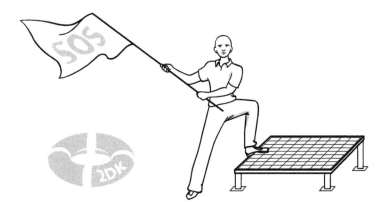

This process can be applied to individual sites but is designed for multiple sites within a portfolio to enable us to compare criticality and create a priority-based order in which to tackle the sites. In each case, there will be a subcategory rating against the various data inputs which we combine in a weighted manner (some areas will warrant intervention more than others). This usually necessitates quantitative and qualitative assessments and testing to determine and justify solutions.

Once this rating has been established, we advise asset owners and operators as to which strategies they should consider and which ones provide estimated performance, reliability, safety and longevity gains, and associated ROI figures. The key to this approach is that each asset is different and should be considered individually, and a consistent approach should be deployed throughout the asset owner's portfolio to prioritise which assets should be tackled first, and which ones are fine ticking over.

The Road2Repower five-step process

2DegreesKelvin's Road2Repower approach includes five steps:

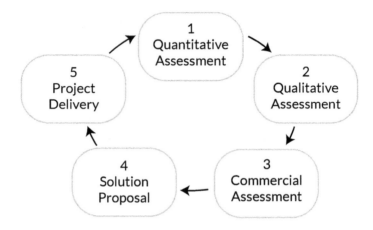

1. **Quantitative assessment:** If you don't know how widespread the problem is, you cannot know what testing methodology and sample size to choose. If it only affects a small number of modules or components on-site, is it worth taking the more expensive next steps? We devise a quantitative survey with an agreed inspection method which will gather evidence to be used if needed at a later stage of the claim or project justification.

2. **Qualitative assessment:** Depending on the issue, the quantities involved and other factors, we will create a qualitative testing and/or investigation procedure that aims to prove or disprove the effect that this issue is having on the performance, reliability, safety or longevity of the asset. We do this through mobile module testing, in-situ EL testing, string, IV, shunt and series resistance

testing, or, in some cases, thorough analysis of the production data and advanced modelling.

3. **Commercial assessment:** Using the outcome of the quantitative and qualitative assessments, we apply the learnings to the asset. We multiply the compounded losses and present an impact model which shows the site owner or stakeholder the power and commercial impacts. This should be backed up with accuracy ranges and assumptions.

4. **Solution proposal:** If the outcome of the first three steps is conclusive, and the accumulated or live losses warrant exploring potential solutions, then we take this penultimate step. There is always something you can do to improve the situation, whether that be a re-design, physical on-site adjustments, retrofittable technology solutions or operational strategy adjustments. It is up to the revamp and repower specialist to outline the solution, its benefits, and how it counteracts the losses or negative operational condition of the asset.

5. **Revamp and repower project delivery:** The site owner or stakeholder responsible for delivering a solution must contract an expert in the field. Revamp and repower projects are notoriously complex, bitty, awkward and difficult, and they require an organisation familiar with data-heavy, system design, quality assurance, high-volume components, team and logistical management, O&M awareness (not to wreck the site), and

technical and commercial strength. This is a specialist market that is only just emerging.

Revamp and repower

The terms 'revamp' and 'repower' are relatively new to the solar PV industry; they describe the measures taken to increase an asset's performance, reliability and life. In some cases, the safety of a system may also be improved or upgraded.

Most solar farms are designed to last twenty-five years. In recent years, I have heard of sites with a design life extending to thirty or even forty years, which I think is pushing it – particularly in climates such as the UK's. Considering the speed in which many sites were – and are still – constructed under subsidy pressure in solar booms around the world, and the relatively imma-ture design, procurement and construction standards employed, my educated guess is that most of this fleet will not last the original design life of twenty-five years without substantial intervention. Systemic failures, premature deterioration and component obsolescence will prevail, along with a deluge of warranty cases, legal adjudications and losses to investors. After all, someone has to pay for it.

There will be a new developing market in revamping and repowering distressed assets with the priority for asset owners being their financial commitments to their shareholders and investors. We can achieve this if we implement engineered solutions which improve performance, reliability and longevity. This is not an easy task, and dabbling will not pay off.

Revamping and repowering may not be a suitable market for traditional EPCs who are used to this scale of project on a fresh and clear piece of land. Although EPCs may contemplate the growing opportunity and dip their toe in, due to the complexity and nature of such projects I feel that their profit margins and risk profiles will jeopardise their long-term domination. Besides, the global new-build market is booming, so why take on bitty, complicated retrofit projects at heightened risk levels?

A few of the O&M main players will likely also throw their hat into the ring to take on emerging revamping and repowering projects, but are these types of companies suitably experienced in delivering complex, technically challenging, data-heavy, high-volume exchange projects? I fear not. They may have done a few corrective-action-based mini projects on assets they manage, but their primary remit is visual inspections and monthly reports. I have spent seven years of my career in O&M, and I know how hard these companies work; from a project delivery perspective, though, I question their resource and technical capacities. They are struggling to keep up with the growing levels of distress already without contemplating larger, complicated revamp and repower projects.

Will TAs take their chances and get involved in this emerging opportunity? They may only enter the engineering side of the arena, offering studies and technical due diligence services to support the market. I doubt that they will have the capacity or appetite to take on the site-based elements of the projects as the risk profiles are too high, and they are not set up for it. Who will emerge as market leaders in the repowering market? What we need as this new market emerges is professional engineering and project management specialists to ensure these complex retrofitted projects are suitably engineered and delivered. These will not be cookie-cutter EPC builds or O&M inspection activities; this market will require a whole new suite of skills, experiences and learnings.

Revamp and repower defined

What do 'revamp' and 'repower' mean?

The term 'revamp' can relate to a range of planned improvements or even optimisation measures which can be applied to a site to increase its performance, safety and longevity, but without major changeouts or exchanges of major components.

Some in the industry may argue that repowering only occurs when you exchange or upgrade the power conversion element of the asset (ie the inverters). However, exchanging a site's modules (the power-generating component within a solar farm) – for example, by replacing 250 W modules with 350 W modules – requires a repowering engineering exercise. This is not just a case of swapping the components over. You'd need to calculate string lengths and configurations and factor in the effects on the inverters and protection settings as well as the interface with the mounting structure, OFGEM and planning considerations. I would also classify this type of project as 'repowering'.

The most common repowering project, although new to the industry, is the exchange of the inverter technology. Since the early 2010s, many inverter brands have come and gone, leaving asset owners with unreliable inverter sets, lowered performance levels, little to no spares, no specialist technical in-house or external expertise or support, and a question mark over the long-term viability of the asset. Most of the inverter repowering projects I've heard about in Europe involve the exchange of a centralised inverter set. The exchange may be 'like for like', where existing inverters are replaced with inverters that have similar power classes, inputs and outputs, and footprints. Others adopt a more interesting and innovative approach, taking advantage of the AC and DC cable design on the site (minimising costs in installing new) and re-designing a centralised string-inverter arrangement, placing multiple string inverters in a single location. This may be a containerised or a building-type structure containing multiple string inverters. This strategy has several advantages:

1. If an inverter goes down, only a small part of the system is not producing, compared to sites with a centralised inverter.

2. In terms of O&M, having all of the string inverters in one place rather than dotted around the field will save time and money in the long term.

3. String inverters are easily fixable and/or exchangeable. O&M companies will hold several spares on-site to minimise downtime.

4. Procurement quality assurance measures can be employed to ensure that the inverter brand's manufacturer is in it for the long term. This would not have been done several years ago.

5. Coupled with in-line IV-curve tracing and module-level real-time analysis, string-inverter systems have several more advanced operational and asset management advantages over their centralised counterparts.

There are other types of revamping and repowering projects which we're likely to see more often in the future, and 2DegreesKelvin are already involved in them in the UK. Let's look at several of these now.

Module orientation and string configuration

A large proportion of the UK fleet were installed in a portrait orientation as that enabled more installed capacity on the field. From an EPC's perspective, the more MWs installed, the more the project is worth. The strings were also strung in a way that was cheap and convenient to install; instead of, for example, twenty-two modules strung horizontally, they were strung in U-type or C-type shapes (eleven on top connected to eleven below), to reduce DC cable return-runs and save money on cable and labour.

There are issues on sites which have these U-type or C-type string configurations. They suffer from more pronounced row-on-row shading losses, as the shading will creep up the lower edge of the bottom row of portrait-oriented modules (particularly in the winter months) and will affect the output power of those modules – and, subsequently, the rest of the modules in the string (even if the rest of the modules are in sunlight). Due to the U-type or C-type string configuration, the shading affects every string on the site.

If the modules were in landscape orientation, shading on the bottom sixth or third of the module would have a smaller impact on production due to the module's bypass diode design. Also, if the strings were strung horizontally the shading loss would only affect the bottom-row modules and strings on-site. The upper rows would remain in full sun and be producing well. Certain inverter sets can be strung with bottom strings and others with tops, or they can be spread out to increase site-wide design efficiencies.

It's possible to gain yield improvements by reconfiguring the module orientation and string design on a tightly packed site, which will generate more power and profit for the rest of the asset's life. In many cases, the exchange for higher-quality DC cable and DC connectors also reduces R_{ISO} faults and inverter trips.

The high number of assets with portrait orientation modules and generally distressed DC systems will force the market to change orientations on these older module technology assets and, in doing so, fully exchange the DC systems. It should be mentioned that the principle of maximising installed capacity on a given land parcel still exists, but due to modern module design (in particular, split-cell technology), row-on-row shading losses are now minimised. Therefore, this revamp / repower project will be limited to the assets installed in the 2010s with more traditional module technologies. Mounting structures may also need modifications, extensions or additional parts to accommodate these changes in orientation.

Horizon-line shading

In many sites over the last few years, I have seen trees, many of which are protected by tree preservation orders, causing horizon-line shading on the southerly and westerly corners of the site, and these trees are causing excessive shading and production losses. These trees and their growth rates could have been accurately modelled during the design phase, but they were not. In the cases I was aware of, tree growth rates were significantly underestimated. What do you do in such a situation? It's only going to get worse as these trees are protected by preservation orders, so you cannot chop them down.

Each site needs to capture an accurate model of the horizon line, and it needs to be represented in a module-level PVsyst simulation to show its true impact on the production of the site. When 2DegreesKelvin does this work, we target areas of the system which are worst affected and design and install focused optimisation technology. We can deploy module- and/or string-based MPPTs to the worst-affected areas to minimise the shading loss effect. Projects that we have worked on have seen 2–3% yield increases from retrofitting this technology to approximately 6–7% of the strings on-site, providing the asset owner with an eighteen-month payback. These types of projects, however, are not plug and play; you will need engineering specialists to conduct a study and design the retrofit details.

PID healing

Potential induced degradation (PID) can result from polarisation and leakage currents on solar farms, and modules in particular. Modules with a negative potential to earth generate an equally high negative voltage between the cells of the module frame. As a result, electrons flow out via the frame and increase the polarisation. This causes cells closer to the frame (outside cells) to start to degrade, and this phenomenon spreads inwards; if left untreated, it will cause catastrophic damage to the module and significantly degrade the module, string and inverter output.

You can identify PID in several ways:

- Extreme cases are visible in data monitoring platforms, comparing strings with each other; lower-producing strings may have a PID effect.

- IV-Curves can detect PID using specialist test equipment to create power curves; in stable irradiance conditions, the irregular shape of the curve would suggest PID.

- The PID effect (checkerboard patterning) shows up in aerial thermography surveys, but unfortunately in some cases other types of operational conditions cause the patterning, so this method is not 100% reliable.

- An emerging method is the application of shunt and series resistance testing. Using specialist test equipment, it provides evidence of the PID effect.

- My preferred way to detect and confidently diagnose PID is with EL testing. This form of testing can detect even early onset PID clearly. It can provide indisputable evidence in warranty claims or when justifying funding a rectification solution – particularly when backed up by flash testing to evidence the power loss impact.

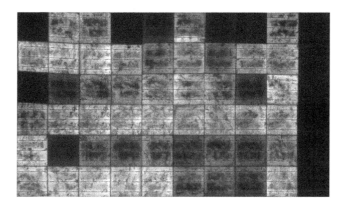

There are several technologies on the market for PID healing. These pieces of hardware connect to the DC circuit on-site and restore the natural flow of electrons by providing a night-time circulation of voltage. Some systems are better than others, and 2DegreesKelvin have a strong partnership with a world leader in this area. As of the time of writing this book, we have installed systems on over 200MWp of solar farms.

Note that PID is everywhere in crystalline modules, even in 'PID-free' modules. The issue is whether the effects are measurable or visible. You can fit PID healing technology to any system, and it would have the biggest effect on modules where PID is mature (in some cases, a 20% increase in restored power), but it would also increase output site-wide by 2–3% on a site with no visible or measurable PID.

There is a strong case for installing these types of technology systems to assets for performance gains alone, not to mention PID prevention for the future. More critically, you can also fit them on sites that are currently negatively grounded, which is a health and safety hazard (ie the systems can disconnect negatively grounded sites, removing the risk of personnel electrocution on-site). PID healing technology is an antidote to module degradation and is currently a good investment in terms of short-term performance gains.

Antireflective module coatings

The last few years have seen the development of proprietary antireflective coatings which can be applied to solar modules to increase light absorption and therefore increase production levels. Although module manufacturers started applying this technology to their glass-fronted modules in the mid-2010s, in most cases there was no antireflective coating on monocrystalline and polycrystalline modules installed between 2010 and 2013 or on most thin-film modules.

These types of coatings are applied to modules and across entire sites, and solution providers boast performance increases of up to 4%. However, this technology is still in its infancy and undergoing trials all around the world to scale up the application process, module warranty effects, and accelerated weathering and deterioration effects.

Warranty claim exchanges

With solar assets ageing worldwide, owners are starting to focus more on product warranties. If the PAC-to-FAC period is over (usually after the first two years of operation), then the EPC no longer has a performance guarantee and often walks away. Whoever takes on the plant at that point takes on the liability for the product guarantees and warranties. At the time of writing this book, the product warranties on modules in particular are approaching their ten-year milestones, so if an asset owner is going to claim, they'd better do so soon.

Many asset owners and operators also do not hold enough spare parts, and these are being rapidly depleted. At 2DegreesKelvin, we have seen multiple cases where, due to lack of spares, different manu-facturers' modules were inserted into strings – in some cases, with different power classes. This causes system inefficiencies and warranty-related risks. This is becoming an issue as module power classes and module dimensions rapidly increase, and asset owners and operators will face more extreme revamp and repower requirements.

From my experience in the UK over the last few years, most warranty claims are related to the modules, with a small number spread over the other main solar system components (inverters, switchgear and trans-formers, cabling, connectors, CCTV systems and the structure). Asset owners look at their modules (and other assets) and see potential PID, delamination, snail trails, discolouration, backsheet issues, junction box issues and other problems, and they think: 'What impact is this having on the performance of the plant and its compounding effect on revenue? And what are our options?' This can initiate the Road2Repower process.

Revamp and repower delivery

Now you know that your asset is a candidate for revamp or repower. You have done quantitative and qualitative assessments to understand the scale and severity of your asset's issue, you know what your options are, and you have a well-thought-through solution proposal and delivery plan. You are ready to contract with a revamp and repower specialist to deliver the project and unlock your returns. The next step is to pull the trigger!

For asset owners considering repowering, or for those who have older assets and want to increase their yield, safety and longevity, be careful about the type of organisation you partner with.

I cannot overemphasise the importance of contracting a professional, technically strong project delivery expert to deliver your revamp and repower projects. If the price seems – heaven forbid – cheap, then there's something wrong. These projects are complex, challenging and will throw up surprises if they are not engineered well. Asset owners must adjust their traditional EPC-poking attitudes and create partnering arrangements to get the best results. Buy cheap, buy twice.

8
New-build Assets

With the world transitioning to renewables, the advancements in solar PV technology and the plummeting prices of solar PV equipment (predominantly modules), subsidy-free large-scale solar is now being deployed more than ever before. Economies of scale are driving the deployment of multi-hundred-megawatt (MW) solar farms across the globe. At the time of writing this book, the largest solar farm in the world is located in China's remote Qinghai province and is a colossal 2.2GW.[23] That's approximately 5.5 million modules, and it can be seen from space. Meanwhile, more and more 20MW+ solar farms are being built in Europe and the US as the project ROIs creep up towards double digits and investors' interest returns to the space.

All of this is great for the economy, bringing profitable power generation to the nations they are deployed in, boosting jobs in the green energy sector and chipping away at the fossil-fuel-to-renewables transition. However, we must ask ourselves:

- Are we developing, designing, constructing and operating these plants as well as we could be?

- Have we considered the lessons learnt from the subsidy-fuelled booms?

- This time, are solar assets going to last up to or even beyond their design life?

- Are investors and asset owners educated in the advantages of investing in quality?

- Has it sunk in that price shouldn't be the focus, and that the quality of the design, the equipment selected, and the construction and operation standards will positively affect their returns?

The jury is still out on these questions, and this is one of my reasons for writing this book. I want to make solar PV investors more aware of past mistakes, show them how to maximise the success and profitability of their future solar PV investments, and get a glimpse into the future of the industry.

New-build market status

Excluding the projects currently under construction, as of Q2 2021 the projected pipeline of new-build, subsidy-free solar PV in the UK is 16.9GWp built over 621 sites.[24] This suggests an average site size of over 27MWp in installed capacity. With most of these sites likely to be built in the medium term (2023 onwards), there is currently approximately 1GWp of solar PV (thirty-five to forty sites) being installed in the UK per year. This tells us that our national solar PV installed capacity will at least triple this decade.

Europe's current installed capacity sits at around 140GWp of solar PV, with some industry experts projecting it will grow to 290GWp by 2025. This is a massive uptake in solar PV and means 25GWp to 35GWp newly installed solar per year.[25]

When we look at solar PV on a global basis, we start to appreciate the scale of the solar adoption movement. In 2021, the global installed capacity of solar PV is around 600GWp. This is set to increase year on year by at least 125GWp to a projected 1.7TWp of solar PV by 2030 – and these are conservative projections. With the world's growing awareness of global warming and climate change, coupled with multiple policy shifts, the numbers are likely to be considerably higher.

All these new solar assets need to be built. The global, continental and national demands for solar technology and solar professionals have never been higher, and they're set to soar. Not only that, but we still think we can click our fingers and get a simple, static solar farm generating away, fit-and-forget for twenty-five years plus. As we've learnt, though, this isn't the case. We cannot carry on installing solar farms without more rigour in development, design, procurement quality and installation standards. We cannot keep buying the cheapest possible cable, connectors, inverters or modules just to make the asset last for the two-year warranty period.

This all starts with the attitude and strategy of the asset owner. Do they want long-term, high-quality, lower-OPEX smart assets which will stand the test of time? The choices they make filter down into the employers' requirements specification, into the EPC design, build and commissioning, and then into the O&M. Let's get it right from the beginning!

With the solar revolution revving through the gears at an unprecedented pace, it's sensible to focus on the new-build process to identify the main players and how they interact. We must also explore how the sector needs to rethink its mindset when it comes to constructing new-build, large-scale assets for the long term.

New-build phase – key players

Although there are exceptions, when a new-build asset is being developed, from receiving planning consent and a grid connection offer to building a new solar farm, there are five main players involved:

1. The developer who has brought the project to a shovel-ready status

2. The asset owner who funds the project

3. An asset manager or technical consultant carrying out the principal designer role and construction oversight

4. A TA providing technical due diligence services, usually for investor sign-off

5. The EPC – the principal contractor who will deliver the project and build the asset

Developer   Asset Owner   Technical Advisor

Asset Manager

EPC

Developers

Let's start with the developer. As discussed in Chapter Six, the independent developer searches for prime land masses which are suitable for large-scale solar and which have a reasonably close and viable connection to grid, a willing landowner and no major risks that the project will not go through planning. Once a site meets the various criteria and gains connection agreements and planning approval, the developer offers a project to asset owners (typically investment funds). Developers may sell the project rights and walk away; they may be tied into the SPV and have a piece of the action; or vertically integrated solar companies may develop in-house, meaning they hand over the project to their construction delivery teams and become an independent power producer (IPP) themselves. For this example, let's stick to the more common case of a developer selling the project rights at shovel-ready status.

Asset owners

The asset owners in a new-build project attempt to add capacity and revenue generation as part of a green energy fund. They have plenty of money to deliver high-quality, technically advanced assets if they wish to, and – supported by their own technically evolved in-house teams – liaise with TAs, asset management companies and other specialty consultants to formulate 'owners' requirements' documents and run competitive EPC tenders. They usually take on the formal role of 'client' for contractual and health and safety purposes.

TAs, consultants and asset managers

There are several reasons why owners use TAs, consultants and, in some cases, asset management companies that generally outsource consultants. In the first instance, they need to check the EPC's design, component selection, pre-designs and bankability. This is called technical due diligence and it usually takes place before the EPC contract signing to assure the owners' investors that the EPC are suitable and sufficient. Then, you may have an asset manager or technical consultancy acting as the principal designer. They will be responsible for coordinating and ensuring that all pre-construction designs and prep-arations are of a high and safe standard. They work between the client and the main EPC contractor. As the project transitions into construction, and then into the commissioning phases, their role develops into an owner's engineer or construction oversight one.

EPCs

The EPC is the main construction contractor who designs, engineers, constructs and commissions the solar farm. They must ensure that the design, compo-nents and construction methods are high quality, and they must deliver the project safely, with minimal environmental impact, and on time and on budget. Once the EPC commissions the plant, they are usually obliged to provide a two-year O&M service. Some EPCs have their own O&M divisions while others outsource O&M services to local, smaller contractors. EPCs usually aim to get out of the two-year warranty period with most of their bond intact and move on to the next new-build project.

Now that we know the players involved in new-build assets and the contractual dynamics between them, where should asset owners looking to grow their portfolios focus their efforts? To answer this, let's review the age-old tussle between capital expenditure and OPEX.

CAPEX vs OPEX

Looking back over my career, through oil refineries and gas terminals, steel works, coal-fired power stations, biomass conversions and energy-from-waste plants, and then into solar PV and battery storage, there has been a consistent focus on capital expenditure (CAPEX) over operational expenditure (OPEX). This is a common theme running through all industries and sectors – after all, the CAPEX is what calls for the investment in the first place. The OPEX is factored into the financial modelling, but often arbitrary norms are inserted rather than a site- and technology-specific rate. Some models even use a completely stripped-back rate with minimal scope, calling off specialist-scope items as and when they are required. The issue here is that driving down OPEX in your models to improve the project ROI is short-sighted and often aims only to secure the funding for the project, rather than factoring in what suits the asset and project life span. You can almost smell the giant bonuses for getting these deals over the line.

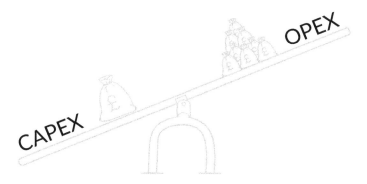

Having been involved in both new-build construction and O&M phases of a solar farm's life cycle, I can appreciate both the importance of build quality and a more generous and realistic scope of work and budget for the O&M contractor. Often these scopes are light and generic, with tight budgets. They place considerable pressures on O&M contractors to provide professional services to get the most out of the site, and often the funds are insufficient to meet the high standards they should aim for.

Investors need to push for design, technology selection and construction quality as their number-one priority and factor into this the site's operability. There are many smart things you can do to minimise O&M costs and provide continuous data and knowledge about the operational health of your site. These include online IV-curve tracing on inverters, online cable temperature monitoring for fire prevention and avoiding the need for hand-held IR inspections, and AI-driven predictive maintenance systems to provide insights into future failures. These measures take the pressure off the O&M so they can concentrate on service excellence in the human-dependent scope items like visual inspections.

I find OPEX currently under-priced and undervalued. Investors and TAs need to give this area of their commercial model more focus to bring sustainable value to the project life cycle. It's not as if you see many portfolio owners who aren't making huge profits. They may be good at squeezing the little guys, but I fear that if they don't adjust their 'big money' attitude they will lose more revenue in production and availability losses than they save by squeezing the O&M scope.

There were many shortfalls in the design of solar farms in the early 2010s, most of which were down to a lack of design pedigree in large-scale solar, sites being designed by the EPCs (who had other commercial drivers besides quality and longevity), and – more critically – the fact that the plants' designers had no historic standards or experience to lean on. After all, solar PV is a relatively new technology, at least at scale. So what do new-build designs need to consider?

Garbage in, garbage out

I have visited many sites in the UK that suffer from horizon-line shading. This means they have (usually) immovable objects, such as trees, around the south boundary of the site which cause shading on the solar array. The site's original design would have included the construction of a PVsyst simulation. PVsyst is an internationally recognised simulation software tool you can use to populate a project with the site details (grid coordinates, installed capacity, module and inverter details, module inclination, row spacings and assumed losses). The software normally uses a database of irradiation data to simulate the annual production and yield for the system. You can then use these details to construct the financial and investment models to fund and build the site. From my observations and network understanding, most of the global fleet of solar farms use PVsyst simulations.

Simulations' accuracy and validity will vary widely depending on the competency of the designer, the information they are provided with, design assumptions and the depth of analysis carried out. In cases that 2DegreesKelvin have checked, sites designed in the early 2010s have inaccurate PVsyst simulations, meaning that all of the asset owners' financial forecasting is wrong. Asset owners are scratching their heads trying to work out what is going wrong with their sites as the PVsyst model is sacred and has never before been questioned.

The following five principles can improve the accuracy of any simulation and therefore any power generation model:

1. **Use accurate horizon-line data** – A detailed scan of the east to west (via south) horizon line should have been incorporated into the shading scene. This information usually comes from topographic surveys conducted in the development phase of a project, but it can be enhanced by a scan of the horizon line with a shade measurement device such as a Solmetric SunEye. In particular, factor in the historical growth rates and ages of trees, which will negatively impact production over the asset's life.

2. **Construct module-level simulations** – The majority of PVsyst simulations are developed with a shading scene which is built to string level and not module level, meaning that there are more assumptions of losses rather than accurate losses. Constructing a module-level PVsyst simulation is more time consuming – not only in the design of the shading scene but also in the computing time

for the modelling – but the accuracy gains and confidence in your model are worth it.

3. **Upgrade your meteorological database subscription** – Standard versions of PVsyst and other modelling programs will supply you with historic meteorological data (temperature and irradiance, in particular). Upgrade your subscription to access more accurate satellite data, which will improve the validity of your model and confidence in the figures.

4. **Use site-gathered meteorological data** – To ensure even more accuracy and confidence, gather data on the site with independent and calibrated meteorological sensors before the site is built. This is already being done on developments around the world (2DegreesKelvin have had two projects doing this under NDA), and it gives the investors complete technical confidence and lower risk profiles for projects.

5. **Use the latest PVsyst software** – 2DegreesKelvin have been involved in repowering studies where the original simulation was woefully inaccurate due to multiple design inputs being wrong or not as-built, and because the simulation was conducted before the site was built – in some cases, up to ten years ago. This introduces significant inaccuracies as the software itself has been updated and improved several times since then. Having up-to-date simulation software and conducting simulations

regularly (every two to three years to ensure assumptions are not slipping) is essential. Inaccuracies are built into the investment model, and therefore the power generation revenue owed to the investors may be offset by the asset's real generation capacity.

6. **Check the competency of the designer or modeller** – Solar PV has been around for decades now, but it wasn't until the 2010s that large-scale solar really kicked off. We have had to learn quickly as the scale and pace of this climate-saving phenomenon's deployment has been unprecedented. It is understandable that mistakes were made, and – with regards to the design and simulation of solar farms – the design norms and budgets and designers' competencies reduced the current operational status of many distressed assets. Therefore, your design team's competency is critical, and you must make decisions for the greater good and the asset's long-term operation, not just the EPC's budget and ease of installation.

Applying these principals will deliver higher standards of design and simulation accuracies for the new-build fleet ahead of us. What else can you do when the designs are complete, and you've ordered your equipment and it's on a cargo ship en route to the site? With modules, there are proactive steps you can take to avoid introducing damaged goods into your brand-new system and maximising life cycle performance.

Why pre-construction module testing is a no-brainer

Recall my cracked egg analogy from Chapter Six: you don't want to pay for damaged goods. Most silicon-based cells used in solar modules are brittle, and subjecting these cells to mechanical stresses is likely to create micro- and macrocracks, which will reduce the operational performance of the module itself, albeit in some cases only as the modules age.

If you could see damage on your brand-new solar modules, would you knowingly and happily install them in your brand-new solar farm? Would you be comfortable having paid for damaged goods? I fear not…

The industry now understands, from our collective experiences over the last decade, that there are three journey phases of solar modules: manufacture, shipment and installation. To avoid introducing any damage or defects at all of these stages, you must commission a robust module procurement quality management strategy. There are multiple points where stresses, damage and defects can be introduced, including:

- Ingot formulation

- Wafer cutting, handling and processing

- Module construction

- Module packing

- Module transportation and shipping

- Module offloading and site distribution

- Module unpacking and handling

- Module mounting

- Module damage in operation

Even small inclusions, stress raisers, or shortcuts at any of these stages can introduce microcracks or defects to the cells. Cracks can propagate to create areas of isolation and power loss, and even small power losses at a cell level can compound as they affect modules, strings and entire sites. This can accumulate over the twenty-five-year project life cycle and combine with the natural ageing and deterioration of the modules themselves, causing the asset owners and investors to lose power over the course of the asset's life. Power relates directly to revenue and profits for individual sites and portfolios, meaning that this is an expensive avoidable loss.

Upstream quality management services

Do your research. Employ specialist, expert consultants to ensure that manufacturers and products are selected using a solid criterion. There are expert companies out there (some of which 2DK partner with) who can go into manufacturing facilities in

Asia to conduct thorough audits and checks on their processes and quality systems and validate the provenance of the various elements of your modules.

The provenance of the cells has historically been one of the underlying quality challenges for purchasers; in many cases, manufacturers buy cells and construct the modules themselves, rather than manufacture the cells from the silicon ingots. As a purchaser, you need to be aware of this as part of your due diligence process.

There are many other checks you should conduct as well, covering back sheets, EVA materials, glass materials and finishes, heating processes, and grid finger and busbar application processes. Without these checks, quality may be lower than you expect.

Any high-quality module manufacturer will have manufacturing-line EL and flash testing test data, which they should provide to the purchaser, and each module will have a unique serial number. This will let you check whether damage has been introduced between manufacture and arrival on-site, and it will provide some confidence in the provenance of individual modules with serial number validation. The quality management expert will also check that module handling, packing and shipping methods are of the highest possible quality to minimise damage.

There is a balance to be struck in terms of how to pack modules (weight and size versus impact on price), but purchasers would like to see robust packing methods to protect their goods. You buy eggs in a 'fit-for-purpose' egg carton; you wouldn't throw them loose into a shopping bag, would you?

The final part of the upstream quality management suite of services will be to arrange independent third-party testing at the point of manufacture or port. This categorically proves whether any defects found were introduced in the manufacturing process. If the test results are clean, then the manufacturer is largely off the hook.

Downstream quality management services

Downstream quality management services are broken down into post-shipment testing and post-installation testing. Together, they are the best-value services as shipping and handling introduce the most mechanical damage. Finding any damage from these processes during testing will serve the asset well.

Depending on the volume of modules coming to a site (lot size) and the purchaser's desired sampling approach, a number of pallets are typically set aside from each container load. A handling team will carefully remove the strapping and boxes from this selection; then, a percentage of the modules within that pallet are tested. These modules are put through a calibrated and certified mobile test laboratory which simulates standard test conditions (1,000 W/m² at 25°C), and EL and flash tests are conducted. Modules are assessed on a cell-by-cell basis against an agreed judgement criteria and module classification system, and modules with excessive damage are rejected. If the number of rejected modules within a single pallet is over an agreed threshold, the second set-aside pallet from the same container will be tested. If this pallet is rejected, as well as the third, then the entire container load is rejected. If not, then the team moves on to the next container.

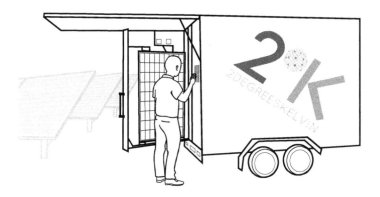

EL and flash data can be analysed and compared with manufacturing data to identify the origin of certain damage, defects and deterioration phenomena.

To ensure that the installation processes are of a high standard and damage is not introduced at the final stage before the modules are on the array, modules can be checked post-installation. During the post-shipment testing, modules are marked with a brightly coloured electric tape which is adhered to the back of the module junction box. A proportion of these modules will be tested with in-situ EL equipment once the modules have been installed.

This process will need to be conducted at night (EL only works at night) and purchasers should consider using a contractor who deploys high-quality tripod systems to ensure EL images are good quality and consistent. Ground-based EL image capture (without tripods) will render low-quality results and distorted images that are difficult to assess. The EL images are compared with the factory and pre-installation EL images to finalise the quality loop and confirm where (if any) damage has been introduced.

Advantages of pre-construction testing

Owners, asset management companies, TAs and EPCs should consider the following advantages of testing pre-construction modules:

- **Pre-selection of premium module manufacturers.** If a purchaser invests in this end-to-end quality assurance process, only premium manufacturers will pass.

- **Higher-power-class cells and modules.** You may get a few more watts per module as manufacturers put their higher-grade modules forward for clients who have a rigorous quality management strategy (and anything they can get away with for those who don't). These small uplifts compound across the entire batch. Even if you had an average of 1 W higher output than the power class, on a 5MWp site this would equate to approximately 18.5kWp extra for free.

- **Clear evidence of where damage, defects and deterioration phenomena originate** and who is liable for them. Thousands of sites worldwide that were built without these quality measures may have damage, but who pays the bill?

- **Minimisation or complete avoidance of costly warranty claim processes.**

- **Enabling a purchaser to get what they've paid for.** Who wants to pay for damaged goods?

- **Preventing the introduction of avoidable power losses** to an asset from day one of production, leading to more production and profits for owners and investors.

- **Creating an asset life cycle record** of module origin, health and status which stays with the asset as it ages, adding value to an asset if it is sold on in the secondary market. 2DegreesKelvin have heard of cases where assets have been sold at up to 5% over the market average.

- **Cheaper lending.** Site owners can obtain cheaper lending rates from funds and investors due to their high-quality approach and reduced risk levels.

There are many ways to introduce defects, damage and deterioration phenomena to modules. Manufacturers, transportation companies, EPCs and O&Ms all need to work smarter to avoid doing so where possible. As we move into a subsidy-free solar world and challenge project ROI, do not scrimp on what's important to maximise the output and longevity of your asset into the future. Invest in pre-construction testing.

Also, put money into the design of your solar farm, and invest in top-quality materials, components and installation teams. Gather data on where everything is on the site and where cables are buried, and never underestimate the value of spending money to determine the provenance of an item or material. The objective is to design and build a solar farm which is reliable, generates high levels of consistent 'bankable' renewable energy and lasts at least the twenty-five-year design life.

As you do with your eggs, take the time to inspect your solar assets for damage, defects and deterioration. It's a no-brainer!

Securing your supply chain

Another big challenge which has emerged, particularly in the UK, is the effect of Brexit on importing materials and products into the country and getting them through customs. The arrangements in place now mean that there are unfortunately more hoops to jump through when importing or exporting between EU countries and the UK. Customs duties, upfront VAT payments, and border securing and compliance checks have caused issues since these changes were enforced. Our recommendation is to employ a competent and experienced customs brokerage service, which will manage the shipments and logistics of your goods through the ports. Even though this is a significant extra cost to your EPC budget, it pales into insignificance compared to likely delay damages costs which you will suffer if you risk going it alone.

9

Lessons Learnt From The UK Solar Boom

Now that we know who's who in the new-build solar industry and committed to focus on design and construction quality, this chapter zooms out again to analyse a subsidy-fuelled solar boom more broadly so we can move forward and learn from its mistakes.

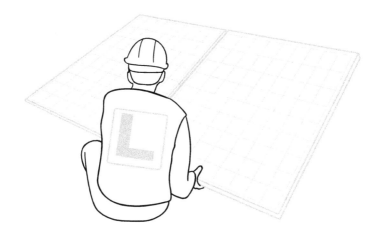

Based on my experiences and my networks, I have identified seven key lessons learnt from the UK solar boom. This list touches on some topics we discussed in previous chapters, and for each lesson I suggest alternative paths which emerging or future markets could take to prevent the same mistakes happening again and to deploy solar in the most sustainable and professional manner.

Lesson 1: Subsidy solitaire

When the subsidies for the first wave of greater than 5MWp large-scale solar came in, developers needed to quickly weigh up the power generation and tariff revenues and compare this to the estimated CAPEX to see if projects were commercially feasible or not.

These sites are now lucrative as subsidies were increased to encourage early adopters, and these tariffs must be honoured for twenty-five years. The lesson for the government and their advisers here is to be cautious about providing what could be described as excessive support based on ultra-competitive adoption of emerging technologies. The FiT and subsequent ROC subsidies did what they were designed to do (encourage and maximise adoption); however, the tax-payer liability is large.

Emerging solar markets should also consider the annual deadline timing for any future subsidy scheme. For the UK market, 31 March couldn't have been a worse deadline. While OFGEM may have thought that positioning the accreditation deadline at the end of the financial year was a sensible idea, this required installing most ground mount assets during the winter, resulting in construction quality, reliability – and in some cases health and safety – issues throughout the fleet. Ground water levels in the UK are typically higher than in mainland Europe, and standing water and muddy conditions hampered many trenching works. Subsequent investigations on multiple sites with existing faults have exposed a lack of industry-standard cable laying (which was understandable in the conditions) and, in some cases, HV cables buried just under ground level. As well as cable installation, the weather also affected water ingress into substation and inverter house basements – which continues to be an issue today – and led to ongoing disputes over electrical equipment and panel IP ratings. If the government of an emerging solar market were to choose a deadline, it should be at the end of the region's summer season.

The final lesson we can learn from the UK's solar subsidy scheme relates to how the ROC subsidies were removed. In the UK, the government underestimated the development and deployment of large-scale solar, and the CAPEX price reduction (predominantly solar module prices) was unforeseen. This meant that once they could remove subsidies due to inflated grandfathered commitments and reducing

CAPEX costs, the government panicked and brought forward the deadline, creating a cliff-edge closure. This caused even more chaos in the final throes of the subsidy period; sites rushed to complete, developers had dozens of sites in the pipeline which needed to be canned, and the solar industry was over in a flash. A considered and gradual removal would have been a more sensible approach.

Lesson 2: Pump-and-dump shovel-ready flips

The consensus among all the different company types involved in the utility-scale sector is that developing solar farms is one of the most lucrative activities in the supply chain (probably second to owning the asset). In other words, for the risk and effort put in, developers make good returns. It is not a risk-free activity – it requires upfront investment and, due to the hit rate, high-rolling developers always need multiple sites in the development pipeline – however, the 'pump-and-dump' strategy that developers deployed during this boom, although commercially lucrative, harmed the solar industry. Substandard specifications, generic planning compliance measures and hungry investment funds wanting scale inflated shovel-ready project sales and made the developers a handsome profit. If the global adoption of renewable energy sources becomes more ethically and environmentally driven, multilayered margins will be frowned on in the future. To minimise the LCOE, choose a vertically integrated organisation that develops the site, builds it, operates it, maintains it and owns it for the long term.

The other contributing factor to the general condition of UK solar farms developed and built during the solar boom was that the designs and system specifications were weak and immature. Many developers cobbled together basic designs and vague material and equipment specifications with their eyes on the prize of maximum profit at a shovel-ready exit. Designs did not consider the long-term operability of the asset, and specifications were not specific enough, meaning the EPCs had free rein to buy cheaper materials and equipment. Additionally, as previously discussed in Chapter Eight, solar development modelling and simulating was only carried out at a basic level, meaning that shading and other loss accuracies were not as accurate as they should be. I recommend that new builds conduct their PVsyst simulations on a module-level basis and engage experienced solar professionals who factor operability into their designs.

During the UK boom, local planning authorities were unprepared for the uplift in solar farm planning applications. Initially, they did not hold any experienced solar personnel and, due to the pressure from government to adopt renewables, many of them did not provide robust enough development and design standards, probably following the path of least resistance to get sites developed, built and operational. Over the last decade, the solar industry's designs, ecological measures and community incentive schemes have come on a long way, and planning authorities in emerging markets should adopt high standards across the board. If we're going to implement solar to last its full twenty-five-year design life, let's do it properly.

Lesson 3: Invest in green and clean renewables

The banking, finance and investment sectors rule the world. They generate trillions in revenue and billions in profit, so it would be naive to think that funds and investors are investing in renewables to save the planet – they are doing it to make serious returns. In the UK alone, the approximately 8GW of utility-scale solar deployed translates to approximately £7 billion invested, based on the diminishing profile of CAPEX prices. Most of these investors have been promised attractive returns for the lifetime of the site, and (with a few embarrassing exceptions) the asset owners are delivering – and then some. Power revenues and subsidy support are generating significant profits, particularly on older sites. I predict, however, that these profits will be short-lived, propped up by higher subsidy rates, and asset owners need to focus on proactive site knowledge enhancement to identify issues before they affect their and their investors' returns. Based on the site inspections I have been involved with over the last decade, I estimate that between 60% and 70% of all installed sites will be generating significantly less than simulated at the ten-year point. Asset owners will require portfolio-wide revamping and repowering investments to maintain returns, and the early adopters of this punchy strategy will be the biggest winners.

In 2010–2012, only a handful of individuals had technical and commercial knowledge and experience in the large-scale solar industry, and they had come to the UK from more mature markets (such as Spain, Italy and Germany). Therefore, for the first half of the UK boom, fund managers and asset owners did not have the technical and practical expertise to know what they were dealing with. They'd been sold a hassle-free, green and clean, money-making machine and didn't appreciate the eventual necessity of investing in solar experts. To all of you asset owners who have just picked up your first few sites in emerging markets, have dreams of owning GWs of solar, and do not know the ins and outs of solar and electrical systems: invest in expertise early. It will pay dividends in the long run.

The other myth to dispel is that 'solar is simple' and that solar is a 'fit-and-forget' technology. To a large extent, it is, but only if implemented correctly. I have come from the utility power sector (coal, biomass and waste), where complex, multidimensional process systems are designed and put into service with 100 times more rigour and engineering consideration compared with solar. You have liquid, gas and powder-based chemicals, pressurised water and steam systems, turbines, pumps and motors, boiling and flash points, enthalpy and entropy, combustion processes and more, even before you get to the electricity hazards. These power generation project developments all have an array of risk mitigation strategies focused on process and personal safety. I have been involved with HAZIDs, HAZOPs, HAZCONs, SIL assessments, FMEA assessments and risk registers for such developments. Though many would argue that solar developments do not need this rigour, applying them raises the standard of design, construction, operation and revenue generation. The emerging UK subsidy-free market is starting to apply these risk mitigation strategies, meaning that HAZOP reviews are in the EPC scope, to factor in more process, performance and human safety considerations to the design and construction phase. For emerging markets, I recommend adopting these approaches from the get-go.

Lesson 4: Just sign it off, Mr TA

Some TA companies – a couple of young consultancies, in particular – have moved on from the UK solar boom period and are doing great work. To them, I say,

'Good on you! Keep focusing on value and investing in expertise.'

When the boom began, the UK-based consultancies and TAs only had a sprinkling of solar understanding and zero practical knowledge of how to design, build, commission and operate solar farms. This is understandable when a new technology emerges and is deployed rapidly. The majority of the 'old-guard' TAs were established engineering consultancies which deployed their services and resources on traditional energy generation projects and thought that solar was a natural transition for them. Lacking their own expertise, they reached out to individuals from more mature markets who did have solar knowledge.

TAs don't have a great reputation in heavy industry generally, and for many of them in the solar industry providing value wasn't at the top of their priority list. Newer TAs focused on the emerging renewables have a suite of report and study templates (which have probably been passed down over the years from one organisation to the next), and then they deploy the optimal resource to get the job done in the most economical way possible – and up their personal utilisation rates. Over the last few years, while 2DegreesKelvin have been providing in-depth site assessments consisting of practical experience-led assessment, investigation, testing and data analysis, on several occasions I encountered teams of graduates (often in a nontechnical subject, such as geography) headed by one engineer with some experience. They walked around the site for two to three hours, took some photographs, and then had the audacity to ask us what we'd found so that they could put it in their report to bulk it up. Unfortunately, the phrase 'money for old rope' comes to mind. My recommendation to anyone commissioning TA services is to do your homework, don't go cheap and try before you buy.

The final lesson regarding TAs is that we must improve on the low standards for technical due diligence, pre-acceptance and final acceptance sign-off in place during the solar boom. As they were in the technical lead role, developers and project and site owners depended on TAs to ensure that what was installed was what they paid for and that the design was sound, the materials and equipment were fit for purpose in the UK (as opposed to mainland Europe), the construction and commissioning standards were industry best practice, and the as-built documentation suite was developed and accurate. The list of responsibilities is long, and the pressurised environment created a perfect storm in terms of varying standards of sites achieving their G59 or G99 connections; thousands of mistakes, shortfalls, defects and missing handover documents being ignored due to looming subsidy deadlines; and TAs collecting healthy fees to deliver substandard work while adding to the price point pressure further down the supply chain.

There is no easy fix, and I admit I'm generalising when I lay all of these issues at TAs' doorsteps. Some TAs – particularly younger, solar specialist ones – are focused on customer value and applying technology to improve it; however, the proof is in the pudding, at least for the majority of sites I have assessed. The standards were not high enough, and stakeholders requiring a TA to fulfil investor needs should check the references and standards of the resource they put on their projects. Geography graduates are no longer acceptable unless they are consulting on geography.

Lesson 5: Focus on CAPEX over OPEX

As discussed in Chapter Eight, the duel between CAPEX and OPEX is longstanding. I have the unique perspective of having been involved in the development process, the design and build process, and the O&M process on the same sites, and I've seen developers focus on their exit price and building pipeline. I've seen the general EPC approach to maximising profits and installing in the most efficient way permissible under the contract. I've also seen the birth of O&M companies who inherited industry-standard and TA-specified O&M scopes which were often static and generic.

But let's be clear: the selection of solar asset equipment and materials are usually dictated by the planning footprint and controls, the connection capacity and the ferociousness of the EPC price competitive environment. If a portfolio owner wants to build a reliable, high-performing set of sites which will last their design life and be worth top dollar, then they invest in the CAPEX, optimising the design, and selecting materials and equipment that are fit for purpose. They invest in pre-construction quality checks to ensure that the site is in perfect condition from day one of operation, and they invest in top-quality TAs to cross-check all these elements. Cutting any of these steps for short-sighted CAPEX savings directly affects the LCOE and reduces the overall project profitability. Skimping upfront will cost you more in the long run. In the UK, we are starting to see the evidence of this; over seven years into the operation stage, CAPEX shortcuts manifest themselves as losses of production, yield, availability, reliability, safety and longevity issues.

We can also improve on the basic design of ground mount solar arrays in the UK. Many site layouts are focused on maximising installed capacity and saving on build materials, cramming as many MWps on the land footprint as possible with minimal materials. In some cases, this makes sense; but in the majority, it doesn't. Designers following commercial instructions and EPC norms laid down array configurations which contributed to higher EPC profits and efficiency build programmes.

With all of this frontloading, including developers, EPCs and TAs, it's the O&M company that has to deal with the scrapings available to operate the plant. The O&M has usually had no input in the design and must find the balance between, on the one hand, being a competent, prudent and professional service provider, and communicating everything to everyone, and, on the other hand, not placing the EPC in hot water over design, equipment, materials and installation standards. Striking this balance is tough, and with the market consolidating small-to-medium-scale outfits are pushed out by multinationals with GWs of scale and large balance sheets.

O&M companies inherited European price and scope norms, and, over the last few years, prices have gone down, and scope expectations have gone up. O&Ms also hold a lot of risk in terms of liquidated damages and on performance, availability, response and rectification times. This has and will continue to put O&M companies out of business. Minimising O&M prices is not a bad thing if the objective is minimising OPEX, but in my view it is short-sighted, and owners will pay for this short-to-medium-term play when the sites mature. Sites are already underperforming because of lack of prudent O&M alone, not to mention design and build quality issues. Owners need to adopt a more 'partnering approach' with their O&Ms and build value-realistic OPEX into their models, supporting them with financial incentives to maximise their value.

The role of asset manager should also come under scrutiny as their role is transitioning from a functional, commercial one to convincing asset owners that they can add strategic and technical value. I agree this change is necessary; currently, most asset managers take zero risk and just administer the power sales and subsidy revenues of sites and portfolios and criticise O&Ms for low performance. The asset owner who finds a professional and forward-thinking asset manager and O&M contractor in a tri-party partnership will win in the end.

Lesson 6: Shake off the module quality delusion

Solar modules are the core technology element of any solar asset. Solar module prices have plummeted over the last ten years, and efficiencies and watt outputs have evolved, driving the accelerated global adoption of this renewable technology. Historically, the purchase price of the modules would have been the biggest collective expense in any solar installation, contributing to over 50% of the total build cost. This percentage is coming down as prices reduce; however, the overwhelming risk emphasis in material and equipment selection is on the modules. The module manufacturing market is competitive and saturated, and many companies have come and gone as it requires massive capital investment and success is not guaranteed. They are all jostling for a position on the Bloomberg Tier-1 supplier list, and while this list is based on the company's financial status and doesn't necessarily reflect the quality of the panels, many companies don't understand this, and they make poor purchase decisions without any proactive due diligence or quality assurance. Material checks, manufacturing facility audits, bill-of-material checks and testing documentation have all been afterthoughts. I am also aware of cases in the early days where the provenance of solar cells, module serial numbers and nameplates were falsified, meaning that testing documents and modules provided did not match. This means that so-called 'Tier-1' modules were purchased in large volumes and installed in the field without any checks, and now we are seeing widespread manufacturing-related defects affecting the output of the site. In recent years, 2DegreesKelvin have worked on sites which need complete replacements of modules due to these defects.

To reduce the chances of this crippling loss during a site's adolescent period, I recommend that developers and asset owners – in addition to focusing on manufacturing facilities and their material selection and manufacturing quality – invest in pre-construction quality sampling to eliminate loss-generating defects from day one of operation. They should apply advanced inspection principles to ensure they are from the right manufacturing batches and facilities and ensure that the shipping and transportation process caused no damage.

As module technology evolves, modules are getting bigger. This makes it more difficult to carry out certain tests (flash tests, in particular) on-site post shipment. New testing equipment is being developed to cater for this; however, EL of a representative sample of modules arriving on-site is widely accepted as best industry practice, and it pays for itself multiple times over in the first year of generation alone – especially when it finds defects and damage, which is often.

The final module-based lesson to focus on for new build is the balance between cheap and effective installation teams and – due to this cheapness or lack of suitable supervision or specified standards – the installation of latent defects from day one of operation. In the UK, it's a topic that causes frequent industrial relations issues. 'British Jobs for British People' is the phrase held aloft on picketing placards. This has created the void between European labour and more expensive equivalent UK labour since Brexit. The solar industry faced three issues when it required labour to install 8GWs worth of solar farms. Firstly, no one in the UK knew how to install solar on a large scale, so we had to look elsewhere. Secondly, British prices for labour are more expensive than mainland European labour rates. Thirdly, some British people are less inclined to do this type of work under such demanding conditions. For these reasons, EPCs often employed cheaper multinational labour pools who would come to the UK and work hard for short, intensive periods (sometimes camping on-site) to get the sites constructed at breakneck speed. Combine the 'job-a-knock' nature of many of these builds with minimal quality standards and installation norms, and, on the majority of sites I have assessed, this haste has led to loss-generating defects everywhere. Although defects introduced in transportation, unpacking, handling and mounting may have been unintentional, improving the awareness, knowledge and supervision of these installation teams would have directly impacted the power generation, project returns and countless hours of finger pointing when defects are found.

Lesson 7: We do it this way in Europe

During the UK solar boom, most of the EPCs I encountered who were responsible for building the solar farms were from the mainland Europe nations with mature solar deployment. From my involvement in multiple installations, I observed a worrying discrepancy between the UK regulatory requirements relating to electrical standards and safety and the practices that some EPCs deployed. The feedback I received from multiple EPCs was that the UK requirements were strict, and if they could get away with doing things the European way, they would. Standards did improve during the solar boom, though. I think most of the contractors and individuals were forced to improve their overall site and construction safety, electrical safety rules, isolation, switching procedures, and cable laying and termination quality. I wasn't aware of many serious incidents during the period – well, none which made the press – but this was more from luck than judgement. Many of the currently emerging markets are in countries that do not have the heritage and advancements in electrical and construction safety that we have in the UK and Western Europe, and this is an area for places like India, South America, China and Australia to focus on.

The European EPCs during the UK boom may have also been surprised to discover the extent of the planning measures they needed to apply to each site. Several told me that the measures for sites in mainland Europe were nowhere near as extensive. UK measures covered wildflower meadows, native hedgerows, wetland and pond restorations, bat-boxes, badger gates, log-piles, beehives and deer-fences, and more. In many cases, these considerations became an afterthought and some sites' failure to plan for them caused issues which need ongoing management for the life of the asset. Wildflower and grass seeding specifications, for example, were heavy-handed and devised by UK TAs and planning authorities. European EPCs were not familiar with these specialist areas, meaning many sites did not factor them into their planning, some planted them incorrectly and others overplanted them. Add to this the specific grass and vegetation management measures which were (and are) often ignored, and you have many sites which are not compliant. The lesson here is for EPCs to get into the detail and make sure they understand the local planning requirements, partner with local specialists and embrace biodiversity.

My final warning for new markets is about resources. As previously discussed, you can only parachute in so much labour from cheaper regions before it starts to affect the quality of the end product. As the market progresses and demand grows for skilled and experienced resources, there will be a requirement for local, regional or national resources which may need developing and more advanced supervision. All of this created a labour vacuum in the UK following the sudden removal of the subsidies; as a result, much of the solar-oriented labour found themselves unemployed and moved on to other sectors. All stakeholders need to be aware of situations like this in new markets. If the UK wants to triple our deployment in the next decade, we need to create a utility-scale-focused competency framework. This is something that 2DegreesKelvin are working on and will bring to market in the near future.

Solar development is never going to be perfect, but if emerging markets and the subsidy-free wave of deployment learn these seven lessons from the UK solar boom, they will maximise their chances of long-term asset performance and solar technology implementation.

PART THREE

THE FUTURE OF SOLAR

Take a breath and try to digest all of the information I've shared with you so far about operational and new-build assets. It's not a simple matter of applying it all and having perfect assets. The revamp and repower market is on the horizon, and asset stakeholders must give themselves enough time to plan for this wave and partner with progressive specialists. We have the past to teach us lessons and the future in which to implement those lessons. We've made monumental strides in green energy production in the last decade, and solar has been a big contributor within the renewable space, but we've only just begun.

Solar PV as a technology, as an industry and as a global movement is evolving in exciting ways. No one would have predicted the progress that the world has made over the last decade. So, what's next for solar PV? Where can it go? Will the future be more of the same, or will new ideas and technology developments help us power the world with the sun?

The final part of this book casts our gaze forward, into the future of solar. What's out there waiting for us and what can we expect? Let's get in our time machine and explore the prospects for solar PV.

10

Committing To A Solar-powered Future

When I tell people what I do and my love for solar, I still hear resistance to change and scepticism over whether renewables can power the world on their own. I hear comments like, 'Those solar farms are popping up everywhere', along with the unfounded belief that, 'Surely we can't build any more'; in reality, there is a lot more we can and should install. Would people rather have big, smoggy power plants pumping out emissions or silent, clean energy from the sun and the wind? Despite the advantages to innovation, there are always naysayers who don't like change.

Quitting non-renewables and going cold turkey

In our quest to save our planet from self-destruction – perhaps the most meaningful of all human endeavours – we also meet resistance. This resistance comes from the organisations, lobbying parties and governments associated with the forms of energy that have been exploited since the industrial revolution. Fossil fuel extraction, refining and combustion have made companies and nations trillions in revenue, and their leaders rely on the profitability, momentum and status quo that these giant machines produce. In many cases, these polluting industries are still subsidised, even though some forms of renewable energy have had their subsidies removed. It's like a drug that they can't quit. Well, it's time to go cold turkey.

In the 2020s, solar PV and wind energy are the energy systems with the lowest LCOE. The majority of the most-polluting nations in the world have committed to reducing CO_2 emissions, with the Paris Agreement and Net-Zero targets coming closer every year, and we have renewable technologies rapidly evolving and advancing, making solar in particular even more efficient and affordable. We also have six of the largest oil and gas companies in the world (BP, Shell, Chevron, Total, Eni and Exxon) pumping billions into renewables projects and investing in existing renewable organisations.[26] Things are shifting. Within the next ten to fifteen years, diesel and petrol cars will be obsolete, solar and wind deployment is likely to at least double in Western countries, and we will no longer need subsidies. Energy prices are likely to soar. Oil and gas refining will remain, but at a smaller scale.

The current targets and trends of governments and the United Nations, as well as global public attitude shifts, are driving these predictions. How can we in the solar industry do our bit to make solar PV the most successful and beneficial technology in the world? What can we do to keep solar assets in operation for their full design life? How do we help the solar and renewables sectors grow and prosper to rid the world of fossil fuels and non-sustainable forms of energy?

We start by adopting the lessons our amazing journey has taught us so far, and then we dare to dream about where the world is heading. Part Three of this book explores ideas, technology developments and mind-sets which the future of the solar sector must consider in a world powered by the sun.

Focus on quality

Now that we are transitioning away from government subsidies and high solar component prices, and EPC prices have dropped enough to spark investors' interest again, it is more critical than ever for the smart asset owner to invest in proactive upstream and downstream quality management services. The focus still is on the solar modules themselves as they make up a large proportion of the CAPEX; they are also the most susceptible to manufacturing defects and damage between manufacturing facility and installation on a solar farm halfway around the world.

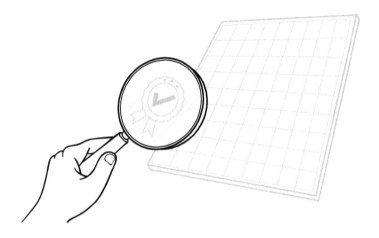

After a decade of solar adoption, we know that if you install low-quality assets, they will not last. If you do not invest in quality, the asset owner will pay the price when they have to revamp or repower their sites after ten years of operation – an expense that wasn't in the financial model.

I can't emphasise enough that, at all stages of the process – from development, design, construction and commissioning, through to O&M – quality doesn't have to cost the Earth, and it will pay dividends for decades to come.

The age of revamp and repower

As I mentioned in Part Two, I predict that the majority of sites built between 2010 and 2020 will not last their design-life period of twenty-five years life without substantial intervention due to systemic and premature degradation and/or failures. Since we know asset revamping and repowering is on the cards, why wait for it to come and give you a nasty surprise? Asset owners should start thinking seriously about the long-term health of their sites, formulating long-term plans, and investing in knowledge gathering, trending degradation and proactive investigations ahead of failures. When would be the optimum time to revamp or repower? If your site can start performing better earlier, then this additional revenue or savings can compound for longer, meaning happy investors and shareholders. The 'fingers in the ears' strategy has not got many more years left – the time to act is now.

The industry is starting to think about what happens at the end of the planning period, and I share my insights about this in the section on decommissioning in Chapter Twelve. It's likely that most sites will be revamped and repowered, and there will be new extensions to planning applications. After all, why would we undo 8GWs of solar on our pathway towards Net-Zero? Some sites will be downsized with technology upgrades; some sites will maintain their current size; and, as the distribution network and national grid infrastructure mature in the decades to come, some sites may even be scaled up and increase in footprint. In all these cases, sites will likely require retrofitting and re-engineering of solar design, technology selections, construction and even operational methods.

When and where to build?

Since the subsidy-driven frenzies have come to an end, the seasonal cycles ending on 31 March each year – which characterised the UK's solar boom and led to an assortment of issues – should be a thing of the past. Now, if you have a choice as to when to build, do it in the summer months. There are so many advantages, the main ones being: drier ground conditions for transportation around and site and civil elements of the project; longer, more productive days; higher morale in your workforce; and lower risks on-site for plant and operative tasks. A developer of a new-build solar farm today needs to think about the systemic issues they will be introducing to an asset if they build in the winter months. Will the additional three to four months of generation in one year significantly outweigh the compounded effects on reliability, availability and performance for the life of the asset? The answer is no.

In terms of where to build, I'm sure you've figured out by now that I quite like solar farms, so when I see one – regardless of where it is – I feel proud that we are making the world a more sustainable place and reversing 100 years of neglect to benefit generations to come. When you choose a building spot, follow planning guidelines and respect areas of outstanding beauty, sites with archaeological ruins, and other ecological and visual impact restrictions, but I see anywhere else as fair game. My number-one factor would be proximity to a suitable network connection, and this has become a major issue in the UK and elsewhere. Old grid and distribution systems were designed for centralised baseload power, not decentralised, intermittent renewables. More about baseload power later in this chapter.

Another big factor for me – particularly in the UK – is flooding risk. A piece of wet, boggy, high-water-table land is generally useless to a farmer. They can't grow crops or graze livestock on it, so you may think, 'Let's make it useful and place solar on it.' It's a sensible and commercially astute conclusion, and it is doable; however, you must be prudent with your site selection and focus on ground water levels and, more importantly, the seasonal changes in water levels. Solar farms installed in drier months have found huge areas of the arrays a foot deep in water for months in the winter, rendering the site inaccessible and unsafe to maintain. If the site has water, manage it with suitably engineered drainage systems. The lack of awareness and foresight around flooding and water levels baffles me when, for less than 0.5% of the CAPEX cost, an asset owner could remove this operational risk on their solar farm. With global weather patterns changing, this risk will only go up.

EPC vs EPC-M

As we transition out of a bloated, subsidy-supported period where solar developments went through multiple discrete service providers, there has been a trend towards vertically integrated solar organisations. Historically, developers only developed and EPCs only built solar farms; now, we see the rise of the integrated organisation that develops, builds and operates solar farms. Such organisations keep profit margins along the supply chain internal and can reduce, or at least share, project risks.

Project owners are also now looking to supply major components into new-build solar farm projects (mainly modules) to the EPC 'free issue'. This creates a saving on the EPC's margin on a component which usually costs over 50% of the CAPEX budget. The EPC will then wrap and deliver everything else. At 2DegreesKelvin, we see this happening more and more as educated project owners are starting to invest in end-to-end quality management services for solar components, and although this is better for the project owner it doesn't necessarily sit well with the EPC. Some EPCs will not be able to generate enough profit from the project if modules or major components are provided free issue, and they will not take part in these tenders.

The next phase of solar deployment will move us from a traditional EPC (engineering, procurement and construction) build model to an EPC-M (EPC management) model. This involves the developer or investor breaking up the project into discrete supply and work packages. They take on the risk for procuring these directly (and may take a small profit themselves), as well as design and performance risk, and then they employ a technical project management company to provide overarching project delivery, package construction management, and possibly delivery of balance-of-plant auxiliary systems. This approach will bring savings for project owners, which will in turn increase the project ROI and in some cases will make projects viable. A project owner implementing this strategy needs a strong technical team and pedigree in solar design and construction, and they need investors who are open to a slightly higher risk level with the potential of higher returns.

Solar + storage = baseload renewables

Along with increasing our awareness of the advantages renewables can bring, the world has also become more educated about their shortfalls and challenges over the past decade. With the projected exponential growth in global demand for energy in the coming decades, and our CO_2 emission levels going up when they should be going down, the pull of 'baseload renewables' has never been stronger for innovators and policymakers.

Coupling renewable energy and energy storage technology seems to hold the short-term answer. Further down the line we have the prospect of hydrogen and safer nuclear, but for now solar, wind, and energy storage technologies exist and are tried and tested on a massive scale. UK battery storage projects are currently being planned in excess of 13GWs of power. These, together with renewables such as solar and wind, are becoming a viable baseload power generation prospect in areas of high demand.[27]

The most advanced and bankable energy storage technology is currently lithium ion. It has gained momentum as the EV industry has developed at pace. Most solar-plus-storage projects use lithium-ion batteries, but there are other options. Innovators and technology developers are continuously working on other battery chemistries and concepts, including sodium sulphur, zinc-air, nickel-hydrogen and vanadium redox flow batteries, each with advantages and disadvantages. The main questions with any battery storage technology are: how long will it last, are they safe, and what do you do with them after you are finished with them?

There are also several energy storage technologies currently racing through the trial process to become commercially viable utility-scale solutions. Two technologies based on the principle of kinetic energy, one from Energy Vault and one from Gravitricity, are worth mentioning here.

Energy Vault has developed a multiheaded crane tower system, which stacks thousands of heavy concrete blocks (35 tonnes a piece) around its central steel structure when energy is cheap or available (charging). When energy is more expensive or needed locally, it unstacks these blocks from height, lowering them with the assistance of gravity to generate electricity at a positive round-trip efficiency (generate). The concept is similar to hydro-generation, which pumps water up a hill to a reservoir and has the potential energy assisted by gravity to drive the water down the hill to turn a turbine. The towers can be built next to existing renewables and can provide a high-reliability, zero-degradation energy storage solution.[28]

Gravitricity is a UK-based technology start-up that has developed a sub-ground kinetic energy construction. It currently uses existing mine shafts or boreholes – and in the future may create purpose-made shafts – to lower and raise a smaller number of heavy weights (up to twenty-four weights of 500 tonnes, totalling 12,000 tonnes) up and down according to electricity demands. This technology has the advantage of creating a small visual impact, since a winch-house building is the only aboveground element.[29]

These types of novel energy storage systems are more sustainable for large-scale applications, both commercially and environmentally. Whichever storage solutions we pursue, they will be the key to unlocking baseload renewables. While nuclear and hydrogen will play their parts in the energy mix of the future, without storage we will fall short.

11

Technology Treats

Solar PV technology over the last decade has focused on making solar panels larger to produce more power, but the efficiency race has also moved forward at pace. How much further can we go? Let's take a look at some of the major solar technology advancements leading us into the future of solar.

Module and cell technology[30]

At the start of the UK solar boom, solar panels were being installed on utility-scale sites with power rating ranges of 200–230Ws, with efficiencies around the 15% mark. At the time of writing this book, in Q2 2021, the highest-power output on a single module is advertised at 660Wp+, meaning power output has almost tripled. Currently, 660Wp panels are over 2.4 m in length, over 35 kg in weight and boast efficiencies of 20.4–21.2%. This is an increase in efficiency of approximately 35%, with a 200% gain in output. During this period, module prices have also at least halved. Unlike microchips, however, the innovation curve of solar technology has a physical limit and they cannot keep getting better and better. There will come a point in the next few years when panels will be impractical to install, negatively impacting the CAPEX price of the solar farm. How far can solar PV technology go? Will we produce a 1,000 W panel? I think we will, but gains after that will likely depend on the rest of the technologies and materials used.

The following cell technologies are at the forefront of module advances.

PERC (passivated emitter and rear cell)

Mono-PERC technology seems to be the standout breakthrough in module design. It has dominated over the last two to three years and is set to become the highest deployment on a global scale. PERC stands for 'passivated emitter rear cells'. It consists of additional layers on the rear side of the cells, which absorb more light and therefore have an increased efficiency and power output.[31]

Split modules with half-cut cells

The purpose of split-cell technology is to lower resistance to increase the panel's performance. They do this by creating the equivalent of two smaller panels with half-cut cells in parallel, so a traditional 60- or 72-cell module becomes a 120- or 144-half-cut-cell module. Recently, manufacturers have begun to produce extra-large 210 mm square cells, which can be cut into three sections; these 1/3-cut cells are used to produce high-powered panels up to 600 W+.

Shingled cells

Another breakthrough in module design is what's known as 'shingled cells'. This is where full-sized cells are arranged in multiple strips and then butted up against each other in a shingle arrangement. These strips are connected with a rear-side adhesive connection, and there are no sunny-side busbar shading losses. This maximises the power-producing area of the panel; hence, higher power output and efficiencies can be achieved.[32]

Multiple/Wire Busbars (MBB)

As PV cells have become more efficient, they are generating more current. During the last decade, manufacturers have transitioned from three busbars to five or six busbars. This shift has also reduced the criticality of microcracks as a lot more current can flow to the busbars. Manufacturers have started to develop multi-busbar (MBB) systems, using up to twelve or sixteen thin, round wires rather than flat busbars. While traditional flat ribbon busbars generate shade on part of the cell, which negatively affects performance, multiple round wire busbars provide lower resistance and a shorter path for the electrons to travel, resulting in higher performance.

IBC cell technology

IBC (interdigitated back contact) cells have a grid of thirty or more conductors integrated into the rear side of the module. As well as looking cleaner and slicker, the removal of busbar shading directly improves efficiencies.

High-density cells

Removing the traditional 2–3 mm gaps between cells increases the total panel surface area that can absorb sunlight. Reducing cell gaps from around 2 mm to 0.5 mm will also boost modules' efficiency and power densities.

Bifacial modules

Bifacial modules produce solar power from both the front (sunny side) and the rear (shaded side) of the panel, usually by having a glass-glass module or a more traditional glass front and a clear backsheet material on the rear. A proportion of light from the sun reflects off the ground and back to the underside of the bifacial module. The brighter the ground colour of surfacing, the more reflection will be absorbed and therefore the more power the bifacial modules will produce. This phenomenon is called 'Albedo', and designers take it into account when designing solar farms with bifacial modules.

How far can solar PV technology go? Will we see a 1,000 W panel? I think we will, but my view is that we won't get much further than that in terms of the core photovoltaic technology. Gains after that will come down to the rest of the technologies and materials used.

Perovskite

One exciting emerging PV-related technology that is starting to build momentum is perovskite. This new material boasts significantly higher power generation properties than traditional silicon-based materials. A company called Oxford PV are currently developing a tandem solution, combining perovskite with silicon, and targeting module efficiencies in the range of 28–37%.[33] This material and approach has the potential to radically change the future of solar PV. Watch this space.

Tracking systems

The module mounting method directly affects the efficiency of the solar panel and the solar plant as a whole. Traditional fixed-tilt mounting structures have been the staple in Western Europe, and in particular in the UK, with trackers representing only a small proportion. With tracking mounting structures, the plane of the solar panel moves during the course of the day to track the sun.

There are two principal types of tracking systems. The first is single axis, which is generally arranged to rotate the modules from facing east in the morning to facing vertically upwards at midday and facing west in the evening. The second type of tracking system is multi-axis, which tracks the sun all day, maintaining a perpendicular angle with the sun to ensure maximum production.

Both deliver significant yield gains, the multi-axis system's being the highest. Although there are many success stories about tracking systems, I have seen images over the years which provided glimpses into tracking system grave years, where the systems didn't work, and a combination of mechanical and control issues rendered the plants out of service. This technology is making great strides to advance and justify its extra expense. Keep an eye out for tracking systems in the years to come; they will have a growing slice of the pie.

Optimisers and sensors

Retrofittable and in-built module and string opti-misers have been around for a few years, but it has taken a while to convince the purchasing parties that they are worth the modest extra cost. They bring substantial advantages, especially for ageing solar farms which have been poorly designed, constructed and maintained. Cell and module voltage mismatch, row-on-row and horizon-line shading, bypass diode failures and other performance-affecting issues are everywhere. There is a strong business case for bringing these module and string optimisation tech-nologies front and centre in the next decade as we squeeze every watt out of our solar farms. Site owners need to learn about the commercial benefits of such technologies in the language they understand: their bottom line.

Sensor technologies are also available to automate online temperature monitoring of various compo-nents, such as DC string connectors, DC fuses in string combiner boxes (SCBs) and HV equipment. This not only acts as a form of predictive maintenance, giving advance warning of potential failures and even fires, but it also will reduce O&M scope and cost. There is no need to conduct thermography inspections on 100% of your SCBs in the summer if you have these data-logging devices.

Inverter technology

Inverters have evolved in parallel to module technology developments, but, from my experience and research, not at the same pace. Inverters are a functional item of equipment which have already been developing for decades in the wider power sector, so although a new solar PV inverter sector has exploded over the last decade or so, the principal technology is pretty mature. For solar inverters, it's all about the advantages they bring to installation and maintenance and wider benefits.

The major leap forward is the ability of multiple inverters on the market to provide live string IV-curve data. This lets you consistently conduct a performance analysis on each string of modules on your park and compare the results. These inverters not only provide crucial performance information, telling O&M companies where to look to rectify issues, but they can also act as a management tool to justify the performance gains of resolution. O&M companies may choose to wait for multiple faults to occur before deciding that travelling to site is justified. Equally, a severe enough issue will call for an urgent response.

Integrated smart inverters will become the norm as we move into the 2020s and beyond, and they will be compatible with other devices and sensors around the park to create huge data clouds of information, which sophisticated data analytics platforms will make sense of. The clear, criticality-based instructions they provide will improve the overall levelised cost of solar energy.

AI, machine learning, analytics and big data

We are now well and truly in the data age, with computing power growing exponentially year on year, and the term 'big data' is being bandied around in most industries. Data is being mined, stored, sold and exploited in almost everything we do that makes a digital footprint. Social media, cookies and search engines are designed to capture your attention, track your activities and convert this attention into sales – and it's working. Data-fuelled digital giants are some of the biggest corporations in the world. If technology and algorithms in software code can influence the choices you make while on your smartphone or laptop, it's not surprising that this tech also has potential in the energy sector and, in particular, the solar PV sector.

Solar assets in the early days of the UK boom had little data monitoring, and what little was installed was limited to providing production output and maybe a few alarms. Data acquisition and monitoring platforms have evolved at incredible speeds over the last decade, and now the market is awash with big industry names as well as more boutique white-label offerings, all boasting the latest in capabilities, machine learning algorithms and predictive maintenance forecasting. Such algorithms can recognise specific patterns in data sets and create mathematical models to simulate them. These models can then make predictions relating to the deteriorating health of a component or subsystem, or even decide whether to send a technician to site based on the payback of the repair compared to the cost of the call out.[34] For me, this is still an area in its infancy, and I have yet to see a system that really impresses me with all of these functions, but I'm confident that it will come.

The natural progression from this technology is 'deep learning', which is an evolution of machine learning that replicates the mechanisms of the human brain to process data. Some asset management companies are developing multi-GW-scale deep learning systems to forecast, predict, and optimise solar assets and portfolios. The possibilities are enormous.

As I stated in the chapter on asset testing and inspection, when it comes to solar assets, knowledge is power; in this context, 'data is power'. This includes not only the operational performance data, which is critical in terms of advanced machine learning systems (voltages, currents, temperatures, irradiance data points, etc), but many other uses for big data coming into the sector, such as construction progress drone imagery, tracking construction progress through the course of the project, and critically defining cable route locations, excavation depths and component counts. It can also be used for maintenance record keeping and hanging every photo, report, test result and reading taken during the asset's twenty-five-year history off a digital twin asset through an interactive portal. Drones are being programmed now to fly around solar farms reading and capturing serial numbers on the solar modules in a semiautomated manner and transferring this data to the digital twin portal. Mind-blowing stuff!

There are additional data-gathering sensors on modules, strings, combiner boxes, inverters and HV equipment such as transformers – all with live data capture to give you a clearer picture of your site's current operational health. The data can even tell you when bird droppings land on a specific module on-site.

Expect to hear more about this area of the market in the future. The larger portfolio owners are all investing in portfolio-wide big data systems which provide value in the form of more information, more time to make decisions, less catastrophic failures and longer-term lower OPEX. If the technology is there, we must endeavour to use it.

Robots and PV

Robotics and intelligent automated systems have long helped industries such as manufacturing to increase efficiencies and reduce human error. In solar, automated manufacturing lines are one of the reasons that prices have dropped so much over the last few years. However, when it comes to installing solar farms and operating and maintaining them, robotics and automated systems are in their infancy.

The prospect of the next generation of robotics is an exciting one. New technologies could provide services for project and asset owners, increasing the quality of data and site knowledge and removing human error and risk of interface with electrical systems.

There is currently a huge amount of R&D going into 'resident-drones'. These are drones that sit on-site in a weatherproof box and, on a regular basis, carry out pre-flight checks; when suitable flying conditions exist, they take off, conduct a survey, upload the data and then land and resume charging. These drones could be fitted with cameras to carry out a range of inspections and capture enough data on a regular basis to build up a 360-degree picture of your asset's operational health. This capability is closer than you might expect, and prototypes are currently being trialled.

There are also automated ground-based robots on the market already; they are not specifically for solar, but they have been adapted to conduct security monitoring duties on solar farms. These robots are fitted with off-road wheels and will be programmed to conduct patrols of the perimeter fence lines with lights, cameras and audio speakers as security deterrents. I can see this being adapted for first response to security incidents on solar farms. Currently security monitoring companies will respond to a camera activation event and, based on what they observe, may send a security guard (keyholding service) to investigate. This is a slow and reactive service which seldom delivers results. Arming each site with a security robot would add a new level of protection.

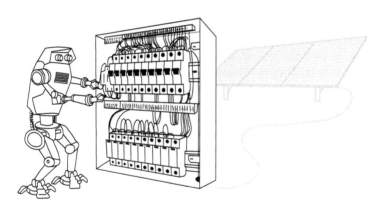

The natural evolution of this idea would be to develop ground-based robots which could carry out visual inspections of modules and other components on-site. This would allow an O&M to carry out the formerly time-consuming, labour-intensive inspections from their control centre. They could capture high-definition inspection video and use intelligent analytics to identify visual issues. These robots' programming can also be overridden, meaning that they can be taken off their routine pathway and sent to investigate issues with live cameras. I can envisage more sophisticated robots with programmable arms, tools and testing devices to enable electrical testing from a control centre. This could eliminate the risk of operative electrocution and let you carry out irradiance-dependent testing when the conditions were right, rather than when your operative was available. This technology could also be adapted to higher-risk activities such as switching switchgear.

The downside to all this automation and robotics is the risk of rendering operatives on-site as surplus to requirements. However, sites will always need human interpretation with the variety of faults, conditions and defects showing up on solar farms, so these field-based roles may transition from vanilla O&M to a more information- and data-management approach.

Blockchain, cryptocurrencies and solar

Most of the developed world has by now heard of Bitcoin: a decentralised digital asset using blockchain technology to carry out peer-to-peer exchanges of value. Much like traditional cash, you can use Bitcoin to buy things online from big brands.

Hard cash currencies, such as pounds, euros and dollars, are known as FIAT currencies. FIAT currencies are generally issued by national or regional governments, but these days they are no longer backed by a physical commodity (such as gold) as they were in the past. They give central banks greater control over the economy because they can control how much money is printed. This money printing can cause the value of FIAT currencies around the planet to plummet in real value, and financial crashes can cause interest rates to soar and hard cash values to depreciate.

Bitcoin is an appreciating asset. It has a finite supply, but it is transitioning towards mainstream adoption. As of Q2 2021, the total market cap of the cryptocurrency space was over $1.4 trillion, with $650 billion of this in Bitcoin alone, and there are those who predict that it will be responsible for the biggest transition of generational wealth in human existence.[35]

Currently, the biggest issue that I see with cryptocurrencies is their hefty carbon footprint. Certain digital coins and tokens are released into the exchange markets through a process called 'mining'. This is an energy-hungry process consisting of computer processing cards solving complex mathematical problems on the blockchain in exchange for a certain coin or fraction of a coin. The sector has taken a pounding from sceptics relating to this energy consumption. It's common knowledge that the total worldwide energy consumption relating to crypto mining is equivalent to the energy consumed in Las Vegas.[36] That's a big energy bill; however, it doesn't take into account the sector's use of renewable sources of energy, which is estimated to be up to a third of its energy and is growing. Also, not all coins and tokens need to be mined; those that don't have a small carbon footprint, particularly compared to Bitcoin. I predict that cryptocurrencies and digital assets will revolutionise multiple industries and in the long term reduce financial markets' carbon footprints. No one is moaning about all the data centres that currently supply all of the financial markets in the world. The key will be to decarbonise it all.

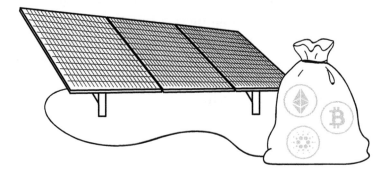

As you probably have guessed from my bullish outlook on Bitcoin, I am an early adopter in the space and am excited about this leading crypto asset and the advancing wave of coins, tokens and use cases which are snapping at Bitcoin's heels. At the time of publishing this book, there are over 10,800 cryptocurrencies in existence, each one designed to deliver a different use case.[37] Use cases include:

- Digital gold (asset of increasing rarity and increasing demand)
- High-speed, low-cost financial transfers
- Financial services (loans, staking, funding, etc)
- Security protocols (equivalent to bank accounts, secure wallets and exchanges)
- Property
- Art
- Gaming and CGI
- Energy (my personal favourite)

As a solar and renewable energy enthusiast, it's the potential use cases in the energy sector and how they could transform the space that interest me the most. These use cases could potentially be developed for peer-to-peer energy trading and Internet of Things (IoT) applications, or even EV charging and e-mobility. The following energy-focused cryptocurrencies are relevant to the solar industry, and I predict they will affect the world's energy transition from fossil fuels:

- **SolarCoin** – SolarCoin (SLR)[38] is the 'world's first solar-energy-backed digital currency'. As explained in the SolarCoin white paper, this digital asset impacts and benefits the entire solar industry value chain, from development through to operations, thereby initiating and supporting the global energy transition. Each MWh of solar energy produced through a solar installation which is signed up to this low-cost, low-carbon, proof-of-stake technology is awarded one SolarCoin to the solar owner.[39]

- **WePower** – As described on their website, WePower (WPR) is a 'platform connecting energy suppliers, corporate buyers and energy producers for easy, direct green energy transactions. The WePower platform provides a streamlined and flexible renewable energy offtaker contracting solution [or digital PPA], which saves time, effort and delivers higher returns to the renewable energy generation facility developers.'[40]

- **Energy Web** – As described on their website, 'Energy Web is accelerating a low-carbon, customer-centric electricity system by enabling any energy asset owned by any customer to participate in any energy market.' To do so, they 'develop and deploy open-source decentralised technologies – the energy web decentralised operating system (EW-DOS)'.[41]

These three are just examples of disruptive blockchain-based technology associated with the crypto space which will streamline traditional ways of buying and selling green electricity.

12
Scaling Solar And The Big 'H'

With multi-hundred-MW or even GW-scale sites becoming the norm, solar PV is starting to compete with traditional baseload power stations. As we saw in Chapter Ten, 'baseload' requires battery or energy storage and this technology needs to develop at a serious pace to ensure that we can generate – and, more importantly, consume – renewable power instead of traditional power twenty-four hours a day, seven days a week.

Sceptics may raise concerns about the footprint demands, the loss of habitats and the blot on the natural scenery, but the alternative to solar and wind is traditional fossil fuel power, which will kill the world. Nuclear has its place, and if we can overcome the expense, safety concerns and excessive development times, then harnessing nuclear energy will contribute to the energy mix in the future, but hydrogen is the one technology which has the potential to be transformational on a global scale. The problem with wind, solar and nuclear is that you cannot use them on industrial sectors or applications which need instant, energy-dense power, such as planes, trains, lorries and ships. The transportation sector is a big negative contributor to climate change. I follow and support the transition towards EVs, but it will always require compromises in range and functionality.

Hydrogen could have it all. It is the most abundant element in the universe (and is therefore sustainable), and it's essentially rocket fuel, so if you can harness its power, it can do virtually anything we need it to do. It can also be made from water through an electrolysis process and has zero direct emissions! The major challenges are that cracking hydrogen and oxygen in water (H_2O) takes electricity, and the ratio of power required to energy produced needs improving if we are going to fully transition to sustainable hydrogen production and use. There is also the question of whether the power used in hydrogen production is renewable or not. 'Blue hydrogen' is produced with fossil fuel power, whereas 'green hydrogen' is produced with renewable power sources. Everyone wants green hydrogen, but with intermittent renewable power such as wind and solar, you would need to pause hydrogen production when the wind did not blow or the sun did not shine, which breaks down the round-trip efficiencies of the fuel. Until we have suitable storage or green backup power to create the around-the-clock production stream, it doesn't make sense to produce hydrogen with just renewable forms of power.

A company called Heliogen is stretching the bounds of what's possible with renewable-powered heat and green fuel production.[42] They use an array of computer-controlled mirrors which reflect and concentrate the sun's rays on to a centralised receiver tower at 1,200 times the concentration of the sun to create ultra-high-temperature heat. This heat can be used to produce power (like more traditional concentrated solar does), provide high-grade heat in the form of superheated steam for industrial processes and produce green fuels such as hydrogen. The production balance can be shared and spread to create a sustainable base-load arrangement to ensure that power, heat and fuel production can work around the clock. We need to see more of these types of commercial-scale technologies, tipping the odds in the favour of green power and energy production.

To visualise how close human civilisation could be to global sustainable power generation, we need only do the maths on how much solar would power the world. Placing one mega solar farm in one location would not meet the demand, as it would not power other continents, but several continental schemes of a set size dotted around the world would fit the bill.

Couple these with a suitable energy storage scheme and, hey presto, sustainable and affordable energy for all.

So, how big are we talking? Approximately 174,000 terawatts of energy consistently strikes the Earth's surface as solar radiation at any moment, even on the cloudiest of days.[43] That means that a single area of approximately 120,000 square miles filled with solar would power the entire world. If we had ten continental mega farms, each one 12,000 square miles, then these would cover an area the size of Belgium or Hawaii. Now, I'm not saying that we should cover entire countries with solar panels, but if we covered the areas of each continent which currently are not suitable for development of any other type, have suitable levels of irradiance, have viable grid connection routes and will have a swallowable impact on the ecology (which can be offset by improvement schemes), then powering the world with solar would be viable. If the world wanted to do this, much like responding to and defeating a global pandemic, then it would be possible.

If we also look to adopt wind, nuclear and hydrogen when it matures, then the scale of solar needed reduces further. If we stopped fossil fuel extraction and placed those funds and subsidies into global-scale renewables, we would power the world in a green and clean way within the next ten years. What's stopping us?

Connection congestion

As we peer into the future of solar PV and renewables in general, and factor in growing energy demands and the transition to EVs, national transmission and distribution networks are currently one of the biggest risks to deployment. In the UK, and in countries all over the world, electricity transmission and distribution systems are struggling to onboard the new wave of intermittent renewables as they were designed for mid-twentieth-century centralised power production, pumping out power around the clock and distributed out far and wide throughout the nation.

Adding intermittent and decentralised solar and wind power into this system has caused major problems for DNOs and National Grid, particularly at the pace of its adoption over the last decade. They have had to shift the way they manage and move the power around the network. They also have growing issues with frequency balancing, over demand and under demand. Compounding these technical constraints is the need to upgrade and improve their infrastructure, as well as governments accelerating support for emissions reduction. To be fair to the transmission and distribution companies, they are in a difficult position, and government support must work closely with them on planning and possibly subsidising major infrastructure upgrades to facilitate our Net-Zero road map.

The direct constraint for any new-build solar asset in the UK, therefore, is connection capacity. Some areas of England and Wales are already congested with solar PV and have shut up shop until future infrastructure upgrades take place. This is a common theme around the world as electrical grid systems start to see the real cost of transitioning from fossil fuels to low-carbon intermittent alternatives.

All landowners and developers must be aware of this connection congestion predicament. It is a 'go/no-go' decision point early in the development process. Governments need to be clear on the criticality of the distribution and transmission networks as they are the key to unlocking a Net-Zero world.

Decommissioning solar farms

Although it may seem counterproductive to talk about decommissioning solar farms in a book about encouraging a new wave of high-quality solar fleets across the planet, decommissioning needs to be factored into any asset's life cycle. In most planning conditions, local authorities will call for the site to be returned to its natural state at the end of the asset's life; however, I believe that the majority of solar farms won't be decommissioned at all and will be revamped and repowered.

Decommissioning is relatively straightforward to plan and execute, aside from the scale and logistical challenges of the volumes of components involved. It's similar in many regards to construction, only in reverse and without the packaging. Just as you would finish a construction project with the connection to the electricity network and by putting subsequent tests and connection agreement measures and controls in place, the first step in a decommissioning project is to disconnect from the electrical network and give all relevant bodies and authorities advance notice of the termination of the electrical generation plant. This will involve keeping records of the final export meter values, much like when you finish with your home electricity supplier. The focus in the first phase of decommissioning will be on making the site safe and removing the risk of electrical hazards under tension. Once that's complete, it becomes more of a dismantling exercise.

My top five decommissioning tips are:

1. Ensure that the local authorities are fully aware of the decommissioning project and submit any health and safety, traffic management or environmental management plans well in advance of the works taking place.

2. Secure a purchaser for the steel work, cable, inverters and HV equipment. This is likely to be scrap values only, but they will stack up.

3. Factor disposal costs into your analysis. If the site you're decommissioning is ten to fifteen years old, the modules likely have some second-hand value, but the effort involved in carefully removing them and packaging them to avoid damage may outweigh the value. However, if your modules are over twenty years old, there will likely be a cost to remove and dispose of them as they are essentially scrap.

4. Consider the physical labour involved to unbolt hundreds of thousands of twenty-five-year-old fixings and extract piles from the ground. This is likely to be more time consuming and expensive than putting them in.

5. Bear in mind that 'leaving the site in the condition it was found in' involves extracting the piles and cable from the ground, and in some cases it may involve significant land remediation works. It is not only unethical to leave piles and cables in the

ground; it is not compliant with your planning duties, will require a significant amount of work (it is much harder to extract the piles if the section above ground is cut off) and could be dangerous for future developments.

2DegreesKelvin have developed our own decommissioning model to enable us to assess specific sites and enter multiple project variables and norms to project future liabilities of decommissioning. There are also many opportunities to save money and also revamp and repower.

13
The Renewables Revolution Continues

The UK has, in recent years, experienced periods where solar (and other renewables) have overtaken traditional fossil fuel power sources, elevating the UK in the world standings in terms of our sustainable and decarbonisation achievements. Looking to the horizon, the biggest goal that we have pledged is our 2050 Net-Zero goal announced in 2019. More recently, in 2021 the UK set a new legally binding target of cutting emissions by 78% from 1990 levels by 2035, building on its previous target of cutting emissions by 68% by 2030.[44]

Unless you've been living under a rock for the last couple of years, you will have noticed the rapid increase in the world's awareness of global warming and its contributing factors. This global movement, which has recently been spearheaded by the likes of Greta Thunberg, Sir David Attenborough and Leonardo DiCaprio, couldn't be timelier. With global environmental tipping points just around the corner, we all must do what we can to turn the situation around and save our world.

Most of us are aware that energy is only part of the problem, and there are things we can all do to make a significant impact, but these measures either cannot be imposed on individuals (not flying or going vegan, for example) or they aren't commercially appealing (like going cold turkey on fossil fuels). For us in the renewables industry, the long-term promotion and deployment of renewables is one of the most achievable steps we can take in the shortest period.

This brings us to my main reason for writing this book: the pressing need to share the lessons learnt and to inform emerging solar markets around the world about what happened in a subsidy-fuelled solar market boom, as well as offer tips for the subsidy-free second wave of developments which is underway. I hope to make stakeholders aware of what will likely happen in any future solar booms, so mistakes can be avoided, and we can achieve high-quality solar PV deployment and mitigate global warming.

100% renewables and a Net-Zero future

Bill Gates, in his book *How to Avoid a Climate Disaster* – which is a must read, by the way – categorises the contributing factors of climate change into five activities:[45]

- Generating energy
- Making things
- Growing things
- Getting around
- Keeping warm and staying cool

Pretty mundane activities, right? All of these everyday human activities are currently creating approximately 51 billion tonnes of CO_2 equivalent (CO_2e) per year, which is warming our atmosphere at an exponential rate. We need accelerated action to get to a Net-Zero future – 'Net-Zero' meaning that these 51 billion tonnes become zero.

How to Avoid a Climate Disaster also explains Gates' pragmatic view on the need for innovation and describes how he assesses new technology and start-up ideas. He recommends asking big questions early, like 'How much of this 51 billion tonnes of CO_2e is this idea going to remove or offset?' It's a pretty sobering reality check that I've given myself when starting my own start-up.

The main takeaway from Gates' book – and my view on the world as we enter the most important decade in human history – is that climate change is vastly complex, both in terms of the technicalities involved in achieving our Net-Zero goals and in the unprecedented scale of the socioeconomic challenges ahead. The population is going to grow, and we will eat more meat and fish. Unpicking decades of bad habits, fossil fuel subsidies and lobbying ping pong will be difficult. There are rough waters ahead and we need to power our industries with green energy sources and decarbonise like never before. The long-term players like nuclear and hydrogen are great to keep developing at pace, but we have to act now – not in ten to fifteen years. Let's take the proven technology we have now and rapidly deploy renewables.

We must also focus on decarbonising the steel, cement and plastics manufacturing industries, the agriculture and fishing industries, and planes, trains and ships. The world population is set to expand from its current 7.7 billion to a projected 11.2 billion by the end of the century, so even if we all maintained our current carbon footprints, we would still be going in the wrong direction.[46] Individual actions are part of the picture, but we need to start taking chunks out of the emission pie. Global energy demand continues to rise, with a 50% increase projected between 2018 and 2050, so we will need green, clean and affordable power.[47]

We also need to consider that, although energy generation is not the biggest single contributor to global warming on its own, when you factor in the energy demands in Gates' other four categories, energy generation is the biggest overall contributor.[48] If we can use green, clean and cheap energy to manufacture products, grow our food, transport ourselves around, and keep warm and cool, then we are getting closer to our Net-Zero goal.

We have an opportunity to avoid a climate disaster, save the world, and do it while being profitable and ethical. With Europe leading the renewables revolution and decarbonising its nations' energy industries, we turn to the rest of the world to follow our lead.

Great news hit the headlines in April 2021: the US not only rejoined the Paris Agreement, but President Joe Biden also committed to aggressive emission reduction targets.[49] There is a long way to go in the US, but if they meet those targets, they will have made a difference. The two countries the United Nations needs to work on now are China and India – numbers one and three, respectively, in emissions to the atmosphere.[50] This isn't a case of bullying them into submission but rather working with them to make historic changes. China and India argue that developing countries have so many relatively young fossil fuel energy generation assets that they cannot simply be closed. The desire is there, but the urgency is not. China predicts a peak of emissions before 2030, and then for them to be Net-Zero by 2060.[51] But by then it could be too late. The damage from those hundreds of billions of tonnes of CO_2e could be the difference between going over our environmental tipping points or not.

We all need to be climate change needle movers and make small changes to our personal and business lives which collectively make a bigger change. With this in mind, here are my top five steps that everyone can take to combat global warming and climate change:

1. **Tweak your diet** – Meat and dairy production through industrial-scale farming of beef, pork and poultry is one of the biggest single contributors to greenhouse emissions in the world. This, combined with the ironically unsustainable 'sustainably caught fishing' industry, is creating a huge imbalance in our ecosystems. Although no one wants to be told what to eat, if enough people reduced their meat consumption to once or twice a week and minimised the consumption of dairy products and seafood, it would have a major positive impact on global warming.[52]

2. **Switch to renewable energy** – The easiest thing to do as an individual, family or business is to switch to a 100% renewable energy supplier. All of the main suppliers (in the UK at least) now have cottoned on to the public's desire to consume

green power, and in many cases, it's cheaper. On top of this, if you can afford it, I would encourage anyone with a suitable roof space to install a solar PV system. You can get some great packages with battery storage and electric car chargers thrown in.

3. **Make your next car an EV** – Another revolution to come out of the 2010s is EV. With Tesla leading the international tsunami of EV cars onto the market, the next couple of years will see increasing EV variety and value. The UK has banned the sale of new petrol and diesel cars from 2030, suggesting that even used petrol and diesel cars leading up to this time will become a liability, and you'll struggle to sell them on.[53] My advice is to make your current petrol or diesel car your last, and make a commitment to your next one being an EV. The infrastructure will catch up, so make the change.

4. **Consume and waste less** – We currently live in a world where we can order anything anytime and it's on our doorstep within twenty-four hours, and our supermarkets and shops are floor-to-ceiling in product choice. Look around the next shop you go into and count items that contain plastic, metal and cardboard. I'm not suggesting you don't buy anything ever again, just be aware of more sustainable options, environmentally responsible products and items with less packaging. In Western society, we have fairly

mature recycling norms, but we can still do our bit to consume and waste less. Rotting waste food gives off methane, which is a large contributor to global warming, so shop with food waste in mind.

5. **Be a climate champion** – Talk, shout and scream about this climate crisis – to your friends and family, to your work colleagues and on social media. Get the message out that people have the will to adapt our lives for the greater good. If you are changing jobs, consider your new employer's green credentials. What are they doing about climate change? If you are starting a business, go climate neutral from day one. There is still a 'tree-hugging' stereotype when it comes to saving the environment, and we need to shrug off this outdated and ignorant stigma and become climate champions!

Conclusion:
The Bigger Picture

I think most of us want what's best for the planet. I'm yet to meet anyone who, deep down, wants global destruction. However, there are still cynics – people who believe it's just another conspiracy, a money-making scheme fashioned by the energy sector or that climate change is part of natural temperature cycles. It's time to wake up. The overwhelming scientific consensus and the widespread effects prove that climate change is happening. If we do not collectively act and change our greenhouse emissions trajectory, the world as we know it will change forever. This is not scaremongering, and this is not me trying to manufacture an environment where my climate change engineering company can make more money; this is a global climate crisis which requires immediate action!

We've got to ask ourselves, what motivates us to do the things we do? Is it money, pride, family, lifestyle, job satisfaction, philanthropy, religion or even fear? It could be any or all of these things, but one thing I'm sure of is that we all want a better world for generations to come. If we all agree that this is our common goal, what a team we will make. The sobering potential of climate refugees, biodiversity extinction, extreme weather events, famine and disease is knocking at our door right now, so we must change our ways, and quickly.

It's all a bit overwhelming, right? What actions can we take to secure our children's future? Well, if you are reading this book, then I assume you are interested in solar, and this is a good start. As well as the general steps I recommended in Chapter Thirteen, when it comes to solar the ultimate takeaway from this book should be 'quality first': quality in design, in procurement, in construction, in commissioning, in record keeping and documentation, in factory inspections, in testing, in O&M, in policymaking and in development. Across the board, we need to make solar the best it can be. Do not settle for average; champion quality and champion solar to secure at least the solar element of our future.

Solar Boom round-up

In Part One, we learnt about solar as a technology, where it has come from and the components which make up a utility-scale solar system. We explored the different solar PV sectors and applications, defined who's who in the industry and delved into the various roles. Finally, we looked at the growing competency gap in the utility-scale solar industry and ways to remedy this with training and competency solutions.

Part Two showed us that the key players in the operational phase of an asset, as well as for the new-build pipeline, need to understand what has not worked well in the past and develop collaborations for a better end result. There are several proactive steps that stakeholders can take to create high-quality solar asset designs and construction standards which will contribute towards world-class power generation long into the future. It's wonderful that we have a decade's worth of hindsight that lets us look back at what we did wrong and, more importantly, make improvements so we can get it right.

Part Three introduced the areas we all need to consider in the future of solar PV and the future of the world. We explored the advantages of making quality our number-one priority, different contractual strategies for developing new-build solar farms, and when and where to build. We outlined some of the technology advancements in hardware, software and blockchain, and the future capabilities of big data and solar PV. We also discussed our route to Net-Zero, the role of hydrogen in our low-carbon future and even decommissioning – quite a wide range of topics which could all have their own books written about them.

Solar, renewables and energy generation are just part of the story. When we look at the other human activities, they all need energy and they all need to be decarbonised. There is much work ahead of us, but together we can do it. Commit to minimising your carbon footprint, and commit to becoming a solar professional and championing quality in the solar industry. Talk about it all with everyone. We cannot succeed unless we share our ideas, thoughts and learnings.

To get the most out of this book, whichever type of company you work for or operate, please see the downloadable Top Tips list at www.2degreeskelvin. org/resources for each of the solar main players. If every reader of this book applies some of these tips, it will make a difference. Please also check out the Further Reading list in this book for more resources with relevant and up-to-date information on solar PV.

I hope you have enjoyed this book and learnt something you can apply to the solar industry and your wider lives. 2DegreesKelvin and I are committed to making a positive change in the world, starting with sharing our insights through this book and our services. If we can make improvements and advancements in the new generation of solar farms being built around the world or encourage people to join this amazing industry, then this book has been a success.

I wish you all a healthy decade in the sun.

Notes

1 'Methane: A crucial opportunity in the climate fight', Environmental Defense Fund (no date), www.edf.org/climate/methane-crucial-opportunity-climate-fight, accessed 15 June 2021

2 A Tabrizi, *Seaspiracy* [film] (A.U.M. Films and Disrupt Studios, 2021)

3 A Winterton, '25 years since the Sea Empress disaster', Natural Resources Wales (15 February 2021), https://naturalresources.wales/about-us/news-and-events/blog/25-years-since-the-sea-empress-disaster/?lang=en, accessed 27 July 2021

4 M Denchak, 'Paris Climate Agreement: Everything you need to know', Natural Resources Defense Council (19 February 2021), www.nrdc.org/stories/paris-climate-agreement-everything-you-need-know, accessed 15 June 2021

5   P Small, 'A brief history of solar power technology', SolarMax (17 August 2015), www.solarmaxtech.com/blog/p.150817000/a-brief-history-of-solar-power-technology, accessed 27 July 2021

6   F Cain, 'How long does sunlight take to reach Earth?', *Universe Today* (14 April 2013), www.universetoday.com/15021/how-long-does-it-take-sunlight-to-reach-the-earth, accessed 15 June 2021

7   'The Sun's impact on the Earth', World Meteorological Organization (no date), https://public.wmo.int/en/sun's-impact-earth, accessed 15 June 2021

8   J Jevahirian, '14 facts about the Sun and solar energy', Michigan Solar Solutions (25 May 2013), www.michigansolarsolutions.com/news/sun-facts_ae394, accessed 15 June 2021

9   'Terajoules of energy used', The World Counts (no date), www.theworldcounts.com/challenges/climate-change/energy/global-energy-consumption/story, accessed 15 June 2021

10   W Kenton, 'The Internet of Things (IoT)', *Investopedia* (28 May 2021), www.investopedia.com/terms/i/internet-things.asp, accessed 27 July 2021

11   'Solar Roof' (Tesla, no date), www.tesla.com/en_gb/solarroof, accessed 15 June 2021

12   'Solar market UK', Power Market (no date), www.powermarket.uk/markets/uk, accessed 27 July 2021

13   *Renewables 2020: Analysis and forecast to 2025* (IEA, 2020), www.iea.org/reports/ renewables-2020/solar-pv, accessed 27 July 2021; D Olson and BE Bakken, 'Utility-scale solar PV: From big to biggest' (DNV, 2019), www.dnv. com/feature/utility-scale-solar.html, accessed 27 July 2021; proprietary database, purchased from Solar Media

14   F Lambert, 'Tesla Model 3 gets a solar roof thanks to Lightyear', *Elektrek* (19 June 2021), https://electrek.co/2020/06/19/tesla-model-3-solar-roof-lightyear, accessed 27 July 2021

15   'What is solar sailing?', The Planetary Society (no date), www.planetary.org/articles/what-is-solar-sailing, accessed 27 July 2021

16   The information in this chapter is based on a LinkedIn article by the author: 'Who's who in the solar industry?' (2 July 2019), www.linkedin. com/pulse/whos-who-solar-industry-john-davies-ceng, 27 July 2021

17   'Distribution network operators (DNOs and IDNOs)', Nationwide Utilities (no date), www. nationwideutilities.com/service/dno-idno, accessed 27 July 2021

18   K Appunn and R Russell, 'Set-up and challenges of Germany's power grid', *Clean Energy Wire* (10 June 2021), www.cleanenergywire.org/ factsheets/set-and-challenges-germanys-power-grid, accessed 27 July 2021

19   E Bellini, 'Single-axis bifacial PV offers lowest LCOE in 93.1% of world's land area',

pv magazine (5 June 2020), www.pv-magazine. com/2020/06/05/single-axis-bifacial-pv-offers-lowest-lcoe-in-93-1-of-worlds-land-area, accessed 27 July 2021

20   Information gained through proprietary database sourced from Solar Media

21   'What is competence?', Health and Safety Executive (no date), www.hse.gov.uk/ competence/what-is-competence.htm, accessed 27 July 2021

22   Information gained through proprietary database sourced from Solar Media

23   E Bellini, 'World's largest solar plant goes online in China', *pv magazine* (1 October 2020), www. pv-magazine.com/2020/10/01/worlds-largest-solar-plant-goes-online-in-china, accessed 15 June 2021

24   F Colville, 'UK solar farm pipeline at 17GW capacity, 58 sites under review for 2021 construction', Solar Power Portal (5 May 2021), www.solarpowerportal.co.uk/blogs/uk_solar_farm_pipeline_at_17gw_capacity_58_sites_under_review_for_2021_cons, accessed 15 June 2021

25   *Renewables 2020: Analysis and forecast to 2025* (IEA, 2020), www.iea.org/reports/renewables-2020/solar-pv, accessed 27 July 2021

26   J Murray, 'How the six major oil companies have invested in renewable energy projects',

NS Energy (16 January 2020), www.
nsenergybusiness.com/features/oil-companies-
renewable-energy/, accessed 15 June 2021

27 N Ford, 'UK solar developers deploy storage
to capture peak returns', *Reuters Events* (2
September 2020), www.reutersevents.com/
renewables/solar/uk-solar-developers-deploy-
storage-capture-peak-returns, accessed 27 July
2021

28 www.energyvault.com

29 www.gravitricity.com

30 Unless otherwise specified, the information
in this subsection of the book is from J Svarc,
'Top 10 solar panels – latest technology 2021',
Clean Energy Reviews (25 March 2021), www.
cleanenergyreviews.info/blog/2017/9/11/best-
solar-panels-top-modules-review, accessed 15
June 2021

31 J Svarc, 'Top 10 solar panels – latest
technology 2021', *Clean Energy Reviews* (25
March 2021), www.cleanenergyreviews.info/
blog/2017/9/11/best-solar-panels-top-modules-
review, accessed 15 June 2021

32 J Svarc, 'Top 10 solar panels – latest
technology 2021', *Clean Energy Reviews* (25
March 2021), www.cleanenergyreviews.info/
blog/2017/9/11/best-solar-panels-top-modules-
review, accessed 15 June 2021

33 'Tandem cell production', Oxford PV (no date),
www.oxfordpv.com/tandem-cell-production,
accessed 27 July 2021

34 A Di Stefano, 'Sun and AI: How solar energy systems can be improved with algorithms', Apro Software (no date), https://apro-software.com/ai-and-solar-energy-systems, accessed 15 June 2021

35 'Today's cryptocurrency prices by Market Cap', CoinMarketCap (no date), https://coinmarketcap.com, accessed 27 July 2021

36 I Ivanova, 'Bitcoin emits as much carbon as Las Vegas, researchers say', *CBS News* (13 June 2019), www.cbsnews.com/news/bitcoin-emits-as-much-carbon-as-las-vegas-researchers-say, accessed 17 July 2021

37 'Today's cryptocurrency prices by Market Cap', CoinMarketCap (no date), https://coinmarketcap.com, accessed 27 July 2021

38 www.solarcoin.org

39 F Sonnet, 'SolarCoin: World's first (solar) energy backed (digital) currency', *Leading Edge Only* (29 December 2020), www.leadingedgeonly.com/innovation/view/solarcoin, accessed 27 July 2021

40 https://wepower.com

41 www.energyweb.com

42 www.heliogen.com

43 'Understand the Sun! 27 fantastic facts about solar energy and solar panels', Chariot Energy (no date), https://chariotenergy.com/chariot-university/solar-energy-solar-panels-facts, accessed 15 June 2021

44　L Blain, 'UK sets world's toughest climate target for 2035', *New Atlas* (20 April 2021), https://newatlas.com/environment/uk-2035-climate-target-78, accessed 15 June 2021

45　B Gates, *How to Avoid a Climate Disaster: The solutions we have and the breakthroughs we need* (Alfred A Knopf, 2021)

46　M Roser, 'Future Population Growth', Our World in Data (first published in 2013, revised November 2019), https://ourworldindata.org/future-population-growth, accessed 15 June 2021

47　A Kahan, 'EIA projects nearly 50% increase in world energy usage by 2050, led by growth in Asia', US Energy Information Administration (EIA) (24 September 2019), www.eia.gov/todayinenergy/detail.php?id=41433, accessed 27 July 2021

48　B Gates, *How to Avoid a Climate Disaster: The solutions we have and the breakthroughs we need* (Alfred A Knopf, 2021)

49　M Denchak, 'Paris Climate Agreement: Everything you need to know', Natural Resources Defense Council (19 February 2021), www.nrdc.org/stories/paris-climate-agreement-everything-you-need-know, accessed 15 June 2021

50　S Davies, *Climate Change: The facts* [film], featuring Sir David Attenborough (BBC, 2019)

51　M McGrath, 'Climate change: China aims for "carbon neutrality by 2060"', *BBC News* (22

September 2020), www.bbc.com/news/science-environment-54256826, accessed 15 June 2021

52   S Davies, *Climate Change: The facts* [film], featuring Sir David Attenborough (BBC, 2019)

53   S Wockner, 'The 2030 ban on new petrol and diesel cars, explained', Greenpeace (20 November 2020), www.greenpeace.org.uk/news/petrol-diesel-cars-vans-2030-ban-phase-out, accessed 27 July 2021

Further Reading

IET, *Code of Practice for Grid-connected Solar Photovoltaic Systems*

SolarPower Europe, *Asset Management Best Practice Guidelines Version 2.0* (23 November 2020), www.solarpowereurope.org/asset-management-best-practice-guidelines-version-2-0

SolarPower Europe, *O&M Best Practice Guidelines Version 4.0* (5 December 2019), www.solarpowereurope.org/om-best-practice-guidelines-version-4-0

SolarPower Europe, *Engineering, Procurement and Construction Best Practice Guidelines Version 1.0*

(24 November 2020), www.solarpowereurope.org/engineering-procurement-construction-best-practice-guidelines-version-1-0

SolarPower Europe, 'Solar Best Practices' (no date), https://solarbestpractices.com

Acknowledgements

I would like to thank my wife and family. Your support allowed me to write this book and follow my dreams. Thank you to my father, Chris, and mother, Jenny: you dedicated your lives selflessly to setting up and supporting me and my sisters. Thanks to my sisters Sarah and Jessica, and your respective families, for all your love and support during my book-writing journey. Thank you, too, to my sister-in-law, Charlotte, and brother-in-law, Ben, for all your friendship, support and listening to me whittle on about my love for solar. Also, to my friends and wider family: for all of your positivity and encouragement, thank you.

Special thanks to Daniel Priestley and Glen Carlson and the whole Dent Global team for your amazing guidance, wisdom and support. Without you and the KPI programme, this book wouldn't have existed. To the Rethink Press team for your fantastic publishing services; it's been a pleasurable journey. And particular thanks to my beta readers, Ypatios, Erik and Arnoud. You provided an amazing amount of constructive feedback, which contributed massively to the end product. Thank you also for your kind words and ongoing support. I owe you all a pint.

Big thanks and congratulations to the 2DegreesKelvin team. It was a real team effort to get this book to market.

Finally, thanks to my network, partners, clients and the wider utility-scale sector for your ongoing support and encouragement. Together we can make solar save the world.

The Author

John Davies CEng is a chartered engineer with twenty years' experience in the energy sector. His career has taken him from the black of fossil fuels, working in oil refineries, and becoming a coal power station manager at age twenty-eight, through to the green of renewables, working in solar since 2012 and launching his own climate change engineering business, 2DegreesKelvin, in 2019. Having been involved in every stage of the large-scale solar PV project life cycle, including development, design, construction, commissioning, O&M, and, more recently, providing advanced engineering solutions to assess, test, improve and optimise solar systems, John is an industry authority and thought leader. He specialises in fleet and asset condition assessment and the latest and greatest technological advancements in the sector to extend solar asset life.

John is passionate about global warming and climate change mitigation and maximising solar PV's potential in our shared battle against the 'old-guard' fossil fuel corporations and short-sighted regimes around the world.

John is an avid single figure golfer who loves to visit the world's best golf courses. He successfully competed in the 2018 Ironman Wales event, where he finished his 3,800 m swim, 180 km bike and 42 km run in 13 hours and 35 minutes.

He lives with his wife and life partner, Sara, in Cardiff, Wales. They have two children, Felix and Florence, who make him extremely proud to be their dad, and a dachshund, Dash. The family love nothing more than film nights at home with a kebab; sun, sea and surf; and travelling around France in their caravan.

Contact

🌐 www.2degreeskelvin.org

📘 @2degreeskelvin

🐦 @2degreeskelvin

💼 @2degreeskelvin

▶️ Search '2DegreesKelvin'